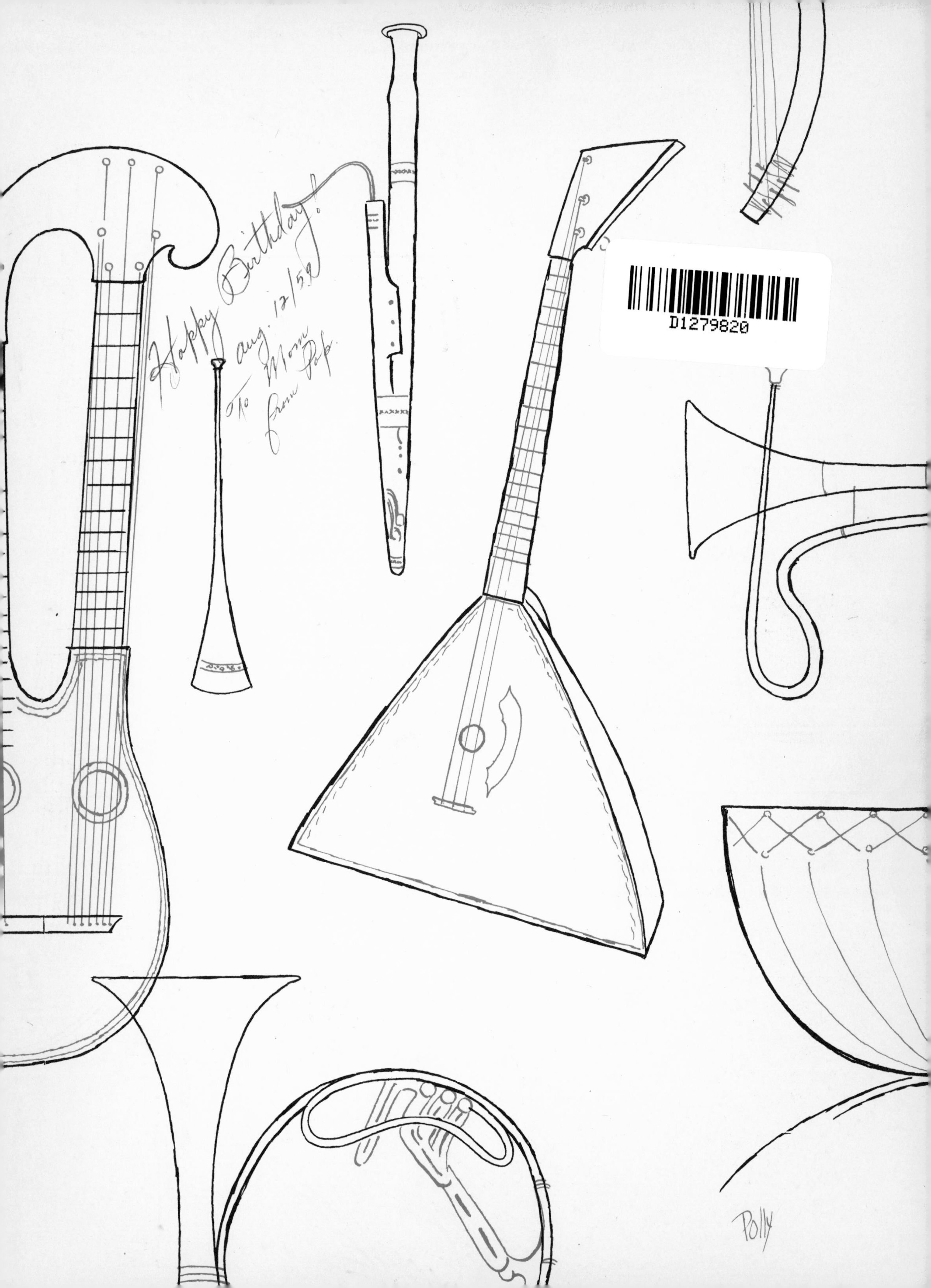
Happy Birthday!
Aug. 12/59
To Mom
from Pop.
D1279820
Polly

MILTON CROSS' FAVORITE ARIAS
FROM THE GREAT OPERAS

Books by the same author

MILTON CROSS' NEW COMPLETE STORIES OF THE GREAT OPERAS

MILTON CROSS' ENCYCLOPEDIA OF THE GREAT COMPOSERS AND THEIR MUSIC

Milton Cross' Favorite Arias from the Great Operas

EDITED BY MILTON J. CROSS

PIANO ARRANGEMENTS BY ALEXANDER STEINERT

TRANSLATIONS BY CHESTER KALLMAN

ANNOTATED BY HENRY W. SIMON

ILLUSTRATED BY POLLY BOLIAN

1958

Doubleday & Company, Inc., Garden City, New York

Library of Congress Catalog Card Number M58-1021

Printed in the United States of America
Designed by Alma Reese Cardi
First Edition

To Lillian

CONTENTS

INTRODUCTION

"The 'Bell Song' from *Lakme,* or the 'Ballatella' from *Pagliacci,* both lovely lilting arias, but, which one shall I add to the list as one of my favorites?" How many decisions like this have I made in the past few months? Selecting fifty of the most beautiful arias from the vast operatic repertoire has been an enjoyable, yet an oft'times frustrating task.

When my publisher first approached me with the idea of doing such a book as this I responded with enthusiasm. Americans seem to thrive on lists and awards—the Bestseller list, the Ten Best-dressed Women, the All-American football teams, the Oscars—and I was only too anxious to add to this great mass of vital statistics my own compilation of most popular operatic arias. Beyond this desire for immortality I had a more practical reason for welcoming the opportunity to compile this volume.

In my more than twenty-five years of broadcasting the Saturday afternoon performances of the Metropolitan Opera Company I have had many requests from listeners seeking information as to where and how they could obtain the works and music of one or more of the numerous arias or operas performed each week. The knowledge that so many opera lovers from all sections of the country were anxious to obtain such a book made me eager to begin.

In the first flush of enthusiasm I jotted down as fast as they came to mind each selection I wanted to include in this book. Within a brief period I was appalled to find that I had listed enough "favorite" arias to fill several volumes the length contemplated by my publisher. It was then, when I realized I could not include every one of my favorites, that the frustration began. I now fully sympathize with that harried breed of man, the editor, whose eternal complaint is that he always has too much material.

Once resigned to my plight, the selection of the final contents turned into a game of mental musical chairs. This aria remained, that one lost out. As with all games certain rules first had to be established. Since this was to be a book for the average opera lover and not the professional musician, each of the arias ideally had to be within range and skill of the average voice—although there would unavoidably be instances where sincere effort would be required to reach a high note, such as the B♭ in the "Celeste Aïda" from Verdi's *Aïda.* And again, since this was to be a popular book, there must be a proportionate representation of arias for each of the four major voice parts—soprano, contralto, tenor, and bass. It was at this point that I decided to add a few duets for both variety and interest. There were of course other considerations, but these were the two main points I kept in mind while making the selections.

The fifty arias and duets in this volume are from thirty-four of the most popular operas in the modern repertoire. Each of the selections is presented in a new simplified piano arrangement, and each features a bright new English lyric. The arrangements were made by Alexander Steinert, and the new translations by Chester Kallman—a very talented collaboration. The only exceptions to this are the arias "Un bel di, vedremo," from *Madama Butterfly,* and "O Mio Babbino Caro" from *Gianni Schicci,* which are reprinted here in their standard versions by the kind permission of G. Ricordi & Co.

In spite of all the windmills I tilted at above, the selection and editing of these favorite arias has indeed been a pleasant experience. I sincerely hope that the wealth of great operatic music within these covers will bring you the many, many hours of pleasure for which it was conceived.

MILTON CROSS' FAVORITE ARIAS
FROM THE GREAT OPERAS

LA HABANERA

FROM CARMEN

BY GEORGES BIZET

LIBRETTO BY HENRI MEILHAC AND LUDOVIC HALÉVY

First performance at Opéra-Comique, Paris, March 3, 1875

Carmen is the most popular gypsy girl in the city of Seville, and at the time the opera opens she is temporarily employed in a cigarette factory. At the noonday recess she follows the other girls out to the square before the factory, and the local swains immediately ask her when she is going to love them. "Maybe never," she replies, "or maybe tomorrow"—and thereupon she sings (and almost dances) her whole simple and straightforward philosophy of love in the *Habanera,* the chorus accompanying her in part of the refrain.

The piece has two stanzas, and during the second she notices the handsome young dragoon, Don José, seated on a stool, whittling on a piece of wood and paying her no attention whatsoever. This inattention at once attracts her, and she does her best to make him look up. Before she returns to work she tosses him the rose she is wearing, much to everyone's amusement but Don José's. He is fearfully embarrassed. We shall hear more about the rose later on.

The name of the tune suggests its origin, and Bizet thought he had based his composition on a folk song from Havana. Later he discovered that the "folk song" had been published by the Spanish composer Sebastián de Yradier, who may or may not have heard it on a trip he made to Cuba. At any rate, Bizet conscientiously credited the composer even though he made very considerable improvements on the original tune.

Allegretto quasi andantino
L'a - mour
Love's a
est un oi - seau re - bel - le Que nul ne peut ap - pri - voi - ser, Et c'est
god on the wing for - e - ver, Who'll bear no bond-age or know of laws; Though you
portando la voce
bien en vain qu'on l'ap-pel - le, S'il lui con - vient de re - fu - ser. Rien n'y
call him he may fly else-where Be-cause he wish - es or just be - cause! Beg him,
port.
fait me-nace ou pri - è - re, L'un par - le bien l'au - tre se tait; Et c'est
threat-en him, bribe or ar - gue If you have plent - y of time to waste! One man

l'au-tre que je pré - fè-re Il n'a rien dit, mais il me plaît.
woos me and ends with no-thing, And one does noth-ing but suits my taste!
espress.
L'a - mour! L'a - mour!
I know love well,
l'a - mour! l'a - mour! L'a-mour est
I know love well! He's ne - ver
en - fant de Bo-hême, il n'a ja-mais, ja-mais con-nu de loi, Si tu ne
known, is ev - er free, And noth-ing's new to him and noth-ing's barred: If you do
p
pp

m'ai - mes pas, je t'ai - me; Si je t'ai-me, prends garde à
not love me, I love you, If I love you, be on your
toi! Si tu ne m'ai - mes pas, si
guard! If you do not love me, If
p
f
p
tu ne m'ai-mes pas, je t'ai - me! mais si je
you do not love me, I love you, But if I
p cresc.
f
p
t'ai - me, si je t'ai - me, prends garde à toi!
love you, If I love you, be on your guard!
f
3
cresc.
f
f
ff

TOREADOR SONG

FROM CARMEN

BY GEORGES BIZET

LIBRETTO BY HENRI MEILHAC AND LUDOVIC HALÉVY

First performance at Opéra-Comique, Paris, March 3, 1875

It is closing time at Lillas Pastia's Café on the outskirts of Seville when Escamillo, a handsome and popular young toreador, puts in an appearance. For his sake the city ordinances are stretched a little. Captain Zuniga of the guards proposes a toast to him, and the bullfighter replies in kind, delivering what is probably the most popular tune in this most popular of French operas. Like the *Habanera,* it has two stanzas with refrain; and as Carmen had directed the second stanza of the *Habanera* at the newly discovered Don José, so Escamillo directs the second stanza of his introductory song at Carmen, whom he sees now for the first time. And as Carmen had directed her movements at Don José, so Escamillo goes through the appropriate pantomime with his cloak particularly to attract Carmen. He is just as successful as she was.

Bizet had originally composed a completely different aria for Escamillo's first entrance in the second act. The story goes that the opera directors did not like it and asked for a more popular type of tune. The present song was Bizet's solution; but Charles Lamoureux, the distinguished conductor, reported that the composer said, on delivering it, "They want filth, and here it is!" The main difficulty in crediting this story, as Olin Downes once pointed out, is that if Bizet considered the tune filth, why should he have used it so often and so effectively in other parts of the opera—in the Prelude and in each of the last three acts?

Allegro moderato
Escamillo:
Vo-tre toast, je peux vous le ren - dre, Se - ñors, se-ñors car a - vec
To your health! To my new com-pan - ions! Se - ñors, se-ñors , A fight - ing
les sol - dats
man am I!
Oui, les To - re - ros peu-vent s'en-ten-dre
Yes, a to - re - ro lives like a sol-dier
sempre
Pour plai - sirs, pour plai - sirs, ils ont les com-bats! Le cir-que est plein, c'est
Whose de - light, whose de - light in com-bat is high! The a - re - na hums with
jour de fê - te! Le cir-que est plein, du - haut en bas; -
ce - leb - ra - tion: When we per - form it is hol - i - day! -

ff
sempre f
Les spec-ta-teurs,_ per-dant la tê-te, Les spec-ta-teurs_ s'in-ter-
The crowd is tense_ with wild ex-cite-ment; still, still more wild_ Will they
pp
rit.
mf
pel-lent à grand fra-cas!_ A-pos-tro-phes, cris et ta-pa-ge-
grow with new_ dis-play!_ Why the fu-ror? Why all the tri-bute?-
f
p
Pous-sés jus-ques à la fu-reur!
What draws them to our grace-ful art?
Car_c'est_ la fê-te
This day's the fes-ti-
du cou-ra-ge!
val of cour-age!
C'est la fê-te des gens de
All sal-ute_ the man of

coeur! Al-lons! en gar-de! Al-lons! al-
heart! The roar! The sil-ence! The pause! The
pp cresc.
dim.
con ritmo
p-f
lons! Ah! To-ré-a-dor, en
charge! Ah! To-re-a-dor, be
dim. molto
pp-f
gar - de! To - ré-a - dor! To - ré - a - dor!
watch - ful! To - re-a - dor! To - re - a - dor!
p Esc. solo
Et son-ge bien, oui, Songe en com-bat-tant, Qu'un oeil noir te re-
Though noth-ing cer-tain can you now fore-tell, Two dark eyes al - so
p

gar — de. Et que l'a-mour t'at-tend, To-ré-a-dor,
watch — and wait with love for you, To-re-a-dor,
leggero
poco rit.
1. a tempo
2. a tempo
l'a-mour, l'a-mour t'at - tend!— tend! To-ré-a-
that will re-ward you well!— well! Your dan-ger-ous
colla voce
dor! To-ré-a-dor! L'a-mour t'at-
game, To-re-a-dor! for love pur-
tend!
sue!

FLOWER SONG

FROM CARMEN

BY GEORGES BIZET

LIBRETTO BY HENRI MEILHAC AND LUDOVIC HALÉVY

First performance at Opéra-Comique, Paris, March 3, 1875

For permitting Carmen to escape while he was conducting her to jail, Don José has spent a month in prison. In Act II he has just been released and has met his beloved at Lillas Pastia's inn. She dances and sings for him, and he completely succumbs to her enchantment—when the bugle call summons him to duty. When he starts to leave, Carmen flies into a rage, tells him that this is no way to love, and flings his cap and saber at him. Deeply hurt, Don José now draws out the withered flower she had flung to him in the first act, on concluding the *Habanera,* and sings this passionate aria. For a moment Carmen is impressed, but only for a moment. "No," she says, "you don't love me, you don't love me," and begins her argument all over again. But it is only the untimely return of Captain Zuniga to the inn that permits her to win her argument and practically forces Don José to join her and her gypsy friends on a smuggling expedition.

The aria represents only one of the many passages in this opera when Bizet throws aside all pretense of writing music with a Spanish flavor and comes up with a thoroughly French—and thoroughly satisfying—tenor aria. At any rate, it would doubtless be thoroughly satisfying if there were ever a tenor conscientious (and skillful) enough to sing the penultimate phrase, *Et j'étais une chose à toi,* as Bizet wrote it—that is, beginning the little scale softly and diminishing the tone gradually till the high note is barely breathed. Instead, it is almost universally sung exactly the opposite way, with a crescendo leading to a high B-flat robustly bellowed. Customarily it brings down the house just as thoroughly as it destroys the composer's lovely musical and dramatic idea.

Andantino
Don José
p con amore
Original in Db Major
La fleur que tu m'a-vais je - te — e, Dans
This flow - er you threw to de - ride me, Re-
pp
ma pri - son m'é-tait res - té — e, Flé - trie et sè - che, cet - te
mained with me in pri - son al - ways; Though dry it kept its rich per-
fleur gar - dait tou - jours sa douce o - deur. Et pen -
fume, Though fa - ded lit the sto - ny gloom. I would
dant des heu - res en - tiè - res, Sur mes yeux, fer - mant mes pau -
close my eyes and would place it On my eye - lids hours in your

pià — res, De cette o - deur je m'en-i - vrais Et dans la
hon — or, And drunk-en on the per-fumed air Through-out the
animando un poco crescendo
nuit je te voy - ais! Je me pre - nais à te mau-
night I saw you there. I tried to curse you or to
animando un poco
pp
a tempo
p
di - re A te dé - tes - ter, à me di - re: Pour -
hate you, I tried to for - get, tried re - peat - ing: "Fate
a tempo
p
quoi faut - il que le des - tin L'ait mi - se
on - ly meant to work my loss When Fate ar-

pp
là sur mon che - min! Puis
ranged our paths to cross." But
dim.
je m'ac - cu - sais de blas - phè - me, Et je
I knew that I was blas - phe - ming For I
pp
cresc. molto
ne sen - tais en moi - mê - me, Je ne sen -
on - ly had one de - sire, And I could
cresc. molto
stringendo
tais qu'un seul dé - sir un seul dé
not be less than true To its one
stringendo

Tempo I
sir, un seul es - poir: Te re - voir ô Car -
hope, I prayed in pain To be with you a -
f
Tempo I
rit.
a tempo
men, oui, te re - voir, Car tu n'a -
gain, You, Car - men, you! One glance of
p a tempo
rit.
p
vais eu qu'à pa - raî - tre, Qu'à je -
yours was all it need - ed, One glance
p
ter un re - gard sur moi, Pour t'em - pa -
that pierced me like a knife, And I sur -
dim. molto

dim.
rer de tout mon ê — tre, Ô ma Car-men!
ren-dered all my be — ing! You must be-lieve
dim.
pp rall.
a tempo
Et j'é-tais u-ne chose à toi! —
I have but one aim in my life, —
rall.
colla voce
pp
a tempo
sempre pp
Car-men, je t'ai — me! —
One wish, to love — you! —
pp
ppp

SOUS LE DÔME ÉPAIS

FROM LAKMÉ

BY LÉO DELIBES

LIBRETTO BY EDMOND GONDINET AND PHILIPPE GILLE

First performance at Opéra-Comique, Paris, April 14, 1883

Pierre Loti, friend of Debussy and French exquisite with a literary style of overpowering charm, made late nineteenth-century artistic circles discover the sensuous delights of the East—at least in books. The opera *Lakmé* is avowedly based on Loti's first great success, a romance originally entitled *Rarahu* and later reprinted as *Le mariage de Loti.* The relationship between the two stories is, however, quite distant—as distant as Polynesia, where Loti's story takes place, is from India, the locale of the opera.

The story concerns the ill-fated love of the beautiful daughter of a fanatic Brahmin priest named Nilakantha and a British officer named simply Gerald (no last name). The first act takes place in the sacred garden of Nilakantha, and near the beginning of that act, his daughter, Lakmé, utters the exquisite duet *Sous le dôme épais* in concert with her slave-attendant Mallika. Lakmé removes her jewelry and, leaving it on a stone bench, steps into a boat with her companion and glides downstream, the two still singing as they disappear from sight.

Original in B major
Andantino con moto
a tempo
Dô — me é - pais
Scar — let rose, —
Sous le dôme é - pais
Where the scar-let rose
mp dim.
poco rall.
a tempo
Ped.
le — jas-min À la — ro - se - s'as - sem — ble.
jas — min white Weave a dome in - ter - twin — ing.
Où le blanc jas-min À la ro - se - s'as - sem — ble.
and the jas - min white Weave a dome in - ter - twin — ing,
Ri — ve en-fleurs frais — ma - tin, Nous ap - pel - lent en -
From — that shore soft — with light We shall drift on re -
Sur la rive en fleurs ri - ant au ma - tin Viens, des-cen-dons en -
From the flow-ered shore in the ten-der light We shall drift on re -

sem — ble. Ah! — glis-sons en — sui-vant
clin — ing. On — that stream in — our boat,
sem — ble. Dou-ce-ment glis-sons de_son flot char-mant
clin — ing. On_a_shad-ed stream in_an_oar-less boat,
Ped. * Ped. *
Le — cou-rant fu-yant, Dans l'on — de fré-mis-
As — it_will, we_float In hopes — we may be_
Sui_vons le cou-rant fu_yant; Dans l'on — de fré-mis-
As_ the cur-rent will, we float In hopes — we may be_
san — te, D'u — ne main non-cha-lan — te,
gran — ted Shores — un-known and en-chan — ted.
san — te D'u — ne main non-cha-lan — te,
grant — ed Shores — un-known and en-chan — ted.

Ga gnons le bord, Où l'oi - seau chan-te, l'oi - seau
Let us be gone, Drift-ing on and on, Dream-ing
Viens, ga-gnons le bord Où la sour - ce dort. Et l'oi-seau
Come, let us be gone, Let us both drift on, On dream-ing
poco rall.
a tempo
pp
l'oi-seau chan - te, Dô - me é - pais, blanc jas-min,
to en-chant-ment! From that shore soft with light
l'oi-seau chan - te, Sous le dôme é - pais Sous le blanc jas-min,
to en-chant - ment! From the flow-ered shore in the ten-der light,
rall.
nous ap-pel lent en-sem ble!
We em-bark for en-chant ment!
Ah! des-cen dons en-sem ble!
We em-bark for en-chant ment!
Ped.
*
Fine

Un peu plus animé
Lakmé:
Mais, je ne sais quel-le crain-te su - bi - te S'em-pa-re de
Still, ev'-ry time that my fath-er must leave us And we re-main
Un peu plus animé
moi, Quand mon pè-re va seul à leur vil-le mau-di-te. Je
here, When I know him a-lone in that un-ho-ly ci-ty, I
trem ——— ble. je trem ——— ble d'ef-froi
trem ——— ble, I trem ——— ble with fear!
Mallika:
Pour que le
That the great
Dieu Ga-ne-ça le pro-tè - ge Jus-qu'à l'é-tang ou s'é-bat-tent joy-
god Ga-ne-sa may pro-tect him, Down to his sha-do-wy pond let us

eux Les cy-gnes aux ai-les de nei-ge Al-lons cueil
go To gath-er the sky-col-ored lot-us Near to the
Lakmé:
lir les lo-tus bleus, Oui près des cy-gnes aux ai-les de
swan with wings of snow, The sky-blue lot-us in pray'r let us
poco rall.
I° Tempo
p
nei-ge, Al-lons cueil-lir les lo-tus bleus. Dô-me é-pais,
ga-ther, Near the swan with wings of snow! Scar-let rose,
Sous le dôme é-pais
Where the scar-let rose
pp
Ped.

UNA FURTIVA LAGRIMA

FROM L'ELISIR D'AMORE

BY GAETANO DONIZETTI

LIBRETTO BY FELICE ROMANI

First performance at Milan, May 12, 1832

The characters represented by operatic tenors are seldom noted for their strong intellects, and of them all, the feeblest intellect is probably that belonging to the hero of *L'Elisir d'amore,* young Nemorino. In his very first aria in the opening act he justly proclaims himself a witless, doltish peasant who does not have the courage or the vocabulary to tell the adorable Adina that he loves her. And when Adina, in a fit of pique, announces that she plans to marry Belcore, the recruiting sergeant, Nemorino enlists in order to purchase a draft of the elixir of love which he thinks may win him Adina after all. He is quite sure that this elixir is doing its work bravely when all the girls in the village suddenly begin to pursue him. What he does not know is that his wealthy uncle has just died, making him a desirable catch, and that this is the circumstance which accounts for his popularity. However, he does have wit enough to play hard-to-get with Adina, and he observes that despite her impending nuptials, she looks pretty unhappy.

It is at this point, in the second and last act of the opera, that he sings *Una furtiva lagrima.* Its subtle expression of tenderness, sympathy, and passion is quite out of character; yet, ironically, it is the great beauty of this one aria which, is largely responsible for the fact that this opera has maintained its popularity for more than a hundred years.

Larghetto
Nemorino: p dolce
Original in Bb minor
U — na fur — ti — va
One fur - tive tear be -
p
la - gri - ma
tray - ing - ly
negl' oc - chi suoi spun - tò:
Told of a grief she would hide.
quel - le fe — sto — se gio — va - ni in
Look - ing on youth — ful hap — pi - ness, Could
vi — di — ar — sem — brò:
she, Yet so young, not a — bide?

p
che più cer — can — do io vo?
What can such en — vy con — fess?
che più cer - can - do io vo?
What would a tear-drop con - fide?
f
m'a — ma, si
I love! But
psub.
m'a — ma, — lo ve — do, lo ve — do.
she — dare — not say that she loves — me!
p
Un so - lo i-stan — te i pal - pi - ti,
Can ten - der feel — ings ter - ri - fy?
p
37

Del suo bel cor sen-tir;
Must love then dal-ly with grief?
I miei so-spir con-
With but my vow-ing
fon-de-re Per po-co a suo-i so-spir: I
faith-ful-ness, Could I Bring her doubts to be-lief? Be-
pal-pi-ti i pal-pi-ti sen-tir Con-
liev-ing me, would she la-ment the less? Would
fon-de-re i miei co suoi so-spir; Cie-lo, si puo mo-
we dis-cov-er hap-pi-ness, Yet fear? All my life hangs in her

rir! Di più non chie-do non chie do; ah!
tear! I know she loves me and yet I, I,
Cie - lo; si può si può mo - rir Di piu non
lov - ing her so much, fear to die! O fur - tive
freely
chie - do, non chie do, si può mo -
tear-drop! I know now that one can
rall. più p
rir, si può mo - rir d'a - mor.
die, That one can die of love!

VERRANO A TE

FROM LUCIA DI LAMMERMOOR

BY GAETANO DONIZETTI

LIBRETTO BY SALVATORE CAMMARANO

First performance at Teatro San Carlo, Naples, September 26, 1835

The individual acts of many nineteenth-century Italian operas bear subtitles, and the subtitle of *Lucia's* Act I is "The Departure." Departure is what its closing duet is about.

Edgardo of Ravenswood is a sworn bitter enemy of Lord Enrico Ashton of Lammermoor, but he is also in love with Ashton's sister, Lucia. About to leave for France, Edgardo has arranged a secret rendezvous in the Lammermoor gardens with his beloved. He tells her that he would like to become reconciled to his hereditary enemy; and when Lucia tells him that this is impossible, he flies into a rage. Lucia, however, calms him with expressions of love; and the act closes as they exchange rings to plight their troth, and they sing the duet *Verrano a te sull' aure.*

In the final act, when Lucia has murdered her unwanted husband, lost her mind, and is singing the "Mad Scene" before the horrified wedding guests, she recalls the happiness of her love for Edgardo. The melody of this duet is then repeated with moving effect.

Lucia:
(sempre legato)
p
mp
pp
Ver - ran —— o a
The warm at -
te sul —— l'a —— u —— re i miei so - spi - ri ar -
ten —— ding bree —— zes Will sigh of long day de -
den —— ti, u - drai nel mar che mor —— mo —
nied —— us, And night —— ly you will hear my
ra, —— l'e - co de' mie - i la - men —— ti. Pen - san —— do
woe. —— Mur - mur from seas that di - vide —— us. If it will

rinf.
ch'io di ge - mi - ti mi pa - sco e di do - lor,
ease your grief to know What more than grief we share,
f
p
Spar-gi un' a - ma - ra la - gri - ma su que - sto
Look on this ring and feel my love A - bout you
accel.
pe - gno al-lor, ah! su que-sto pe - gno al-lor, ah!
ev' - ry - where. Ah! Love will be with you there! Ah!
f accel.
f
stringendo
Su que-sto pe — gno al - lor, ah! su quel
Love will be with you there! Ah! Love will
f string.

Lucia:
Tempo I
pe - gno al - lor
reach you there!
Edgardo:
p
Ver-ran — o a te sul — l'a — u — re i
The warm at - tend — ing bree — zes Will
Tempo I
pp
miei so - spi - ri ar - den — ti, u - drai nel
sigh of long days de - nied — us, And night — ly
fp
pp
mar che mor — mo - ra — l'e - co de' mie - i la-
you will hear my woe — Mur-mur from seas that di-

men ti. Pen - san do ch'io di ge mi - ti mi
vide. us. If it will ease your grief to know What
rinf.
pa scoe di do - lor, spar-gi un'a - ma ra
more than grief we share, Look on this ring and
Lucia
string.
spar gi su que sto pe gno al - lor, ah!
Love will be a - bout you ev' ry - where, Ah
Edgardo
la gri - ma su que sto pe gno al - lor, ah!
feel my love a - bout you ev' ry where. Ah!
f string.

cresc.
su questo pe gno al - lor, ah! su
Love will be with you there! Ah! Love
su que - sto pe gno al - lor, ah! su
Love will be with you there! Ah! Love
cresc.
que - sto pe gno al - lor, ah! que - sto
will be with you there! Ah! Love will
que - sto pe gno al - lor, ah! que - sto
will be with you there! Ah! Love will
f
Più Allegro
pe gno al - lor!
reach you there!
f
pe - gno al - lor! Io par to!
reach you there! It's time now!
Più Allegro
f

Lucia:
Edgar: rall.
Ad - di o.
Ad - di o.
Ram-
E-
colla parte
non tanto
men ta ti, ne strin ge il Ciel!
ter nal ly our love Makes us one!
Both:
Ad di o!
Ad di o!
f
f

NEMICO DELLA PATRIA?

FROM ANDREA CHÉNIER

BY UMBERTO GIORDANO

LIBRETTO BY LUIGI ILLICA

First performance at Teatro La Scala, Milan, March 23, 1896

In the opening act of the opera, which takes place just before the French Revolution, Gérard is a servant hopelessly in love with the aristocratic daughter of the family, Madeleine de Coigny. By the time this number is sung in Act III, the reign of terror is ruling Paris, and Gérard is one of its powerful leaders. His rival for Madeleine has been his friend the revolutionary poet Andrea Chénier, who in Act II has spared Gérard's life. But now Chénier is under suspicion, and Gérard is in a position either to save his erstwhile friend or to bring him to trial and almost certain death. The soliloquy, which Gérard sings in the chamber of the revolutionary tribunal, magnificently projects his wavering and conflicting powerful emotions. At the close of the aria Gérard signs the indictment, which actually turns out be Chénier's death warrant.

Unlike most of the numbers in this collection, *Nemico della patria?* is more a *scena* than an *aria.* That is, its form is dictated by its dramatic requirements, not by conventional canons of musical form, and an instrumental transcription, without words, would strike the listener as being almost shapeless. Nevertheless, when sung, it can be overpoweringly effective, both dramatically and musically.

Andante a piacere
Ne-mi-co del-la pa-tria?! È vec-chia fia-ba che be-a-ta-
A trai-tor to his coun-try?! A shab-by fa-ble Still be-lieved in
p col canto
f
men-te an-cor la be-ve il po-po-lo.
blind-ly and deep-ly by the pop-u-lace.
Faster
a piacere
Nato a Cos-tan-ti-
Born in Con-stan-tin-
pesante
col canto
no-po-li? Stra-nie-ro? Stu-diò a Saint Cyr? Sol-
o-ple? An al-ien? Went to Saint Cyr? A
da-to? Tra-di-to-re! Di Dumou-riez un
sol-dier? Trai-tor two-fold! With Du-mou-riez, con-
a tempo ff

a piacere
com-pli-ce! È po-e-ta? Sov-ver-ti-tor di cuo-ri e di co-
spi-ra-tor! And a po-et? Cor-rup-tor too of hearts, mo-rale and
p affrett.
col canto
stu-mi!
or-der!
meno
più lento
sempre p
sf
sf
sf
dim.
pp
Un di m'e-ra di gio-ia pas-sar fra gli o-dî le ven-det-te,
My joy once was in liv-ing a-mong these hat-reds And re-ven-ges
p
pu-ro in-no-cen-te e for-te! Gi-gan-te, mi cre-dea! Son sem-pre un
pure-ly, a-loof-ly, strong-ly A gi-ant, so I thought. I'm still a
f
p
p
p

ser-vo! Ho mu-ta-to pa-dro-ne! Un servo ob-be-dien-te di vio len-ta pas-
serv-ant, With a dif-fer-ent mas-ter! I'm now the de-based ser-vant of vi-o-lent
f
p
f più stretto
sio-ne! Ah, peg-gio! Uc-ci-do e tre-mo, e men-tre uc-ci-do io
pas-sion! O ba-ser! I kill now And trem-ble; for while I kill I am
p
f
pian-go! Io del-la Re-den-tri-ce fi-glio pel pri-mo hou-
weep-ing! Li-ber-ty was to be my gòd-dess, My long pre-
dim.
sf
p
di-to il gri-do suo pel mon-do ed ho al suo il mio gri-do u-
oc-cu-pa-tion, Once I heard her and ad-ded My voice in in-vo-
p

rit.
a tempo
ni - to. Or smar-ri-ta ho la fe-de nel so-gna-to de-sti-no?
ca - tion. Have I lost all the faith of that ex-alt-ing de-ci-sion?
mf col canto
p
rall.
Co-m'era ir-ra-di-a-to di glo-ria il mio cam-mi - no!
I walked a road made bright by The glo-ry shed by my vi - sion!
rall.
f
p
La co-scien-za nei cuor ri-de-star de le
In their fu - ri-ous love I saw man-kind a-
ff dim
pp
gen - ti Rac - co-glie-re le la-gri-me dei
wak - ing And suc-cour-ing with broth-er-hood The

vin - ti - e sof - fe - ren ti!
bea - ten, the lost, the ach ing!
animando
Fa - re del mon - do un Pan the - on! Gli
Earth would be - come a Pan the - on Where
animando
mf cresc.
uo - mi - ni in dii mu - ta - re e in un sol
men would live as gods to - geth - er, And love in
f
ba cio, e in un sol ba - cio e ab -
tri umph, And love in tri - umph
f

brac - cio tut - te le gen ti a
still Would goad all hu - man it y
affrett.
mar!
on!
e in un sol
O Love in
ba cio e abbrac - cio tut - te le gen ti a -
tri umph still, In cite us for ev er
poco rall.
mar!
on!
ff
a tempo

CHE PURO CIEL

FROM ORFEO ED EURIDICE

BY CHRISTOPH WILLIBALD VON GLUCK

LIBRETTO BY RANIERI CALZABIGI

First performance at Hofburgtheater, Vienna, October 5, 1762

Orpheus is a subject that has fascinated dozens of composers, perhaps because he was a great musician. Of all the versions composed—from the earliest opera on record, Jacopo Peri's *Euridice,* to Darius Milhaud's contemporary work—Gluck's is the only one that is often presented. Gluck originally composed the role of Orfeo to be sung by a *castrato* on Vienna's Italian opera stage; but when he revised it for Paris, where such singers were not in fashion, the role was rewritten for a tenor. In most countries today, excepting France, the Italian version is usually used and the role is sung by a woman.

In the second scene of the second act, while traveling through the underworld in search of his beloved wife Euridice, Orfeo enters the Elysian fields, where the blessed spirits dwell in serene happiness. So deeply enchanted is he with his physical surroundings that he sings the aria *Che puro ciel, che chiaro sol!* The orchestral accompaniment is particularly eloquent in this aria, seeming to paint the delights of all the natural surroundings.

Andante
Che pu - ro ciel! che chia — ro
How pure the sky! How fresh the
sol! che nuo — va
sun! How calm — ly
lu - ce è que - sta mai! che
luc - id, the liv - ing air! What
dol — ci lu - sin - ghie - ri suo — ni dei
lim — pid half - re - mem - bered mus — ic Through

bei can - to ri a la ti s'o - don
all the val ly en dear ing Wakes the
qui in ques-ta val! dell' au-re il su - sur -
soul's for-got-ten bliss! The tran-quil wind re -
rar, il mor-mo - rar de'
plies: the streams Re - ply in
ri vi, al ri - po - sar e - ter - no
mur murs; and all in - vite to their e-

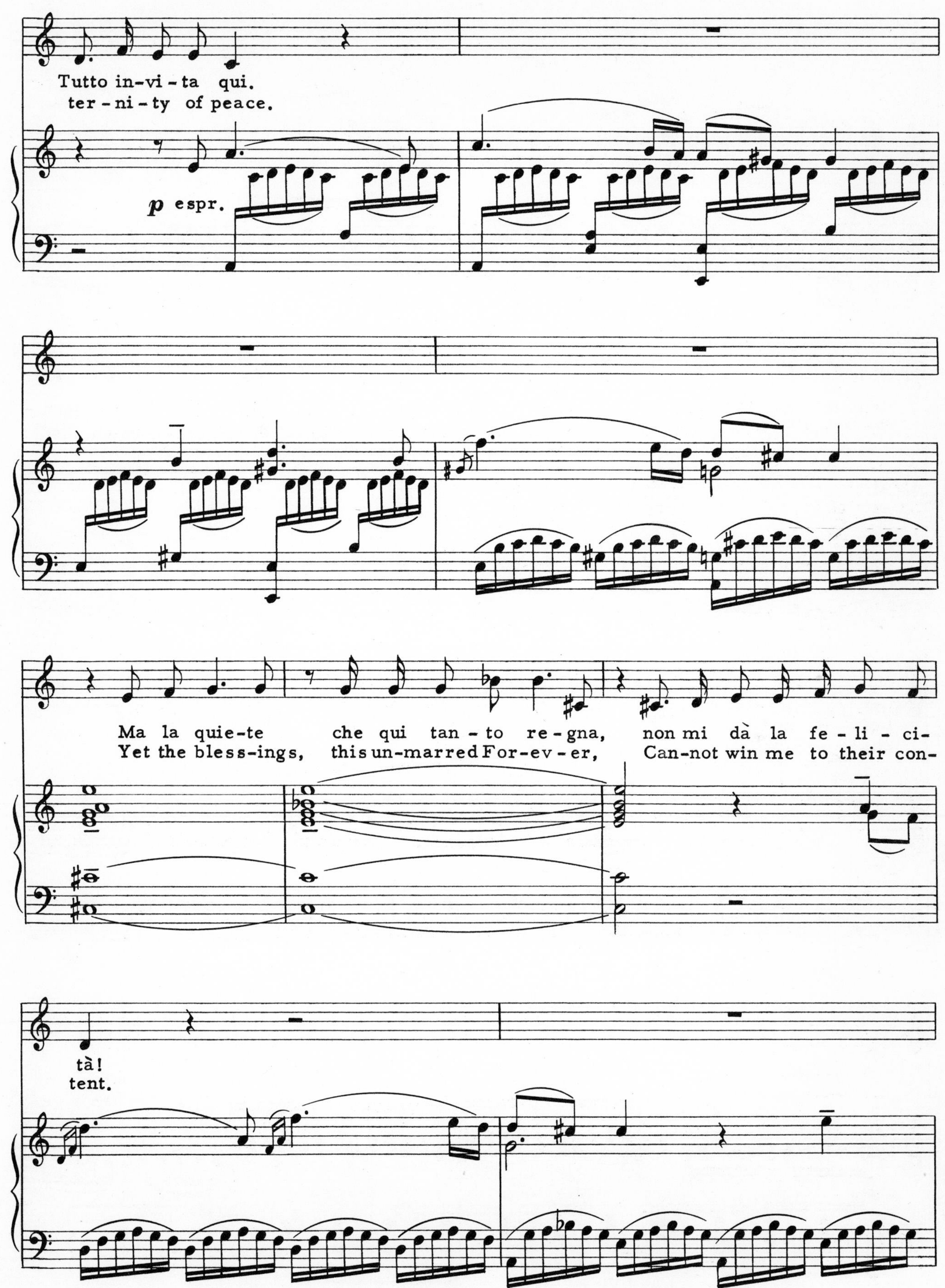
Tutto in-vi-ta qui.
ter-ni-ty of peace.
p espr.
Ma la quie-te che qui tan-to re-gna, non mi dà la fe-li-ci-
Yet the bless-ings, this un-marred For-ev-er, Can-not win me to their con-
tà!
tent.

Sol -
You,
tan-to tu, Eu-ri-di-ce, puoi far spa-rir dal tri-sto cuo-re mio l'af-
my Eu-ry-di-ce on-ly Can woo my rest-less heart From sol-i-tude and
fan — no!
sha — dow!
espr.
I
Your

tuoi soa — vi ac — cen — ti
voice, dear — ly fam — il — iar;
glia — mo — ro — si tuoi squar — di,
Lov — ing, spi — ri — ted glan — ces;
un tuo sor - ri — so
Your smile in - spi — ring,
so — noil som - mo ben — che chie - der vo - glio.
Can a - lone re — quite — my heart's de - sir - ing!
cresc.
f

CHE FARÒ SENZA EURIDICE

FROM ORFEO ED EURIDICE

BY CHRISTOPH WILLIBALD VON GLUCK

LIBRETTO BY RANIERI CALZABIGI

First performance at Hofburgtheater, Vienna, October 5, 1762

In the concluding act Euridice has been restored to Orfeo on one condition—that he does not look back upon her as he leads her from the underworld back to earth. Unfortunately Euridice is not apprised of the terms of the bargain and keeps complaining of her husband's apparent lack of interest in her during the trip. Unable to bear her recriminations, Orfeo turns to her—only to see her fade back into death. He thereupon utters this most moving and in many ways most difficult aria.

Gluck's operatic tale departs from Greek mythology in restoring his wife to Orfeo. The older and sterner tale returns Orfeo to Thrace unattended by Euridice; and there his constant laments so irritate the local women that they tear him to pieces.

The difficulty referred to above in singing this aria does not lie in width of range or other unusual demands upon the vocal chords but in the matter of style and the problem of repeating a long melody with a controlled strengthening of intensity. Not many modern singers are up to it.

Andante con moto
p
Che fa - rò sen-za Eu - ri - di - ce, do-ve an-drò sen-zail mio
My Eu - ry - di - ce is lost now, Now is lost be-yond re-
p
fp
ben? che fa - rò do-ve an - drò, che fa — rò sen-za il mio -
call; How can I vain-ly go on, When my ve - ry life is
sf
sf
ben, do-ve an-drò sen-za il mio ben? Eu - ri -
gone? Los-ing her I have lost all. I who
f
fp
di - ce, Eu-ri - di - ce, oh Di - o! ri — spon - di!
love you, I have slain you! Oh, ans-wer, my Eu-ry-di-ce!

Adagio
ri - spon di! Io son pu - re il tuo fe -
A - wak en! May I not once more re -
cresc.
f
p
de - le, son pu - re il tuo fe - de - le il tuo fe -
gain you? Can you not be Once more from si - lence
fp
fp
Tempo I
de - le. Che fa - rò sen - za Eu - ri - di - ce, do - ve an - drò sen - za il mio
tak - en? No, Eu - ry - di - ce is lost now, Now is lost be - yond re -
Tempo I
p
fp
ben? che fa - rò do - ve an - drò che fa - rò sen - za il mio
call; How can I vain - ly go on, When my ve - ry life is
sf
sf

Moderato
ben, do-ve an-drò sen-za il mio ben? Eu-ri-di-ce! Eu-ri
gone? Los-ing her, I have lost all! I who love you, I have
Moderato
di-ce! Adagio Ah! non m'a-van-za più soc-
slain you! My hopes have crossed Ob-liv-ion's
Adagio
cor-so, più spe-ran-za nè dal mon-do, nè dal
riv-er, Fled for-ev-er To sus-tain you Though I
Tempo I
ciel! Che fa-rò sen-za Eu-ri-di-ce, do-ve an-
fall! My Eu-ry-di-ce is lost now, Now is

drò sen-za il mio ben? che fa — rò do — ve an-
lost be-yond re - call; How can I vain-ly go
sf
cresc.
drò che fa - rò sen - za il mio ben? do ve an-
on when my ve - ry life is all! How shall
sf
mf
drò, che fa — rò che fa — rò sen — za il mio
I vain-ly go on? Los - ing you I have lost
sf
cresc.
sf
sf cresc.
p
ben, sen - za il mio ben, sen - za il mio ben?
all, I have lost all, I have lost all!
ff
f
ff

AVANT DE QUITTER

FROM FAUST

BY CHARLES GOUNOD

LIBRETTO BY JULES BARBIER AND MICHEL CARRÉ

First performance at Théâtre Lyrique, Paris, March 19, 1859

When *Faust* reached London, four years after its Parisian première, it was given in Italian. So much was the composer impressed with the young baritone, Charles (later Sir Charles) Santley, who sang the role of Valentin, that he composed the present aria for him to introduce into the following season's production. As this production was given in English, it happens that the words were originally written in that language by the distinguished critic Henry Chorley. They begin with the line "Even bravest heart may swell." Mr. Kallman has provided, for this volume, a paraphrase of Pradère's French translation of the original.

The aria was interpolated into the second scene, the "Kermesse" scene, and it lends an ironic touch to the well-known tale. For Valentin expresses his love for his sister and his fears that all may not go well when he is not there to guard her. Later on, when he finds out that things have not gone well, he curses her.

Most baritones take the last few notes of the aria an octave higher than they are written, and some even interpolate a high A-flat.

Andante
A - vant de quit - ter ces lieux,
God, in whom all hopes a- bide,
espr.
p
Sol na- tal de mes a- ïeux,
Now that I must leave her side,
A toi Seig-neur et
I to Thy po- tent
Roi des cieux,
grace con-fide
Ma soeur je con- fi e.
My sis- ter's pro- tec tion.
Dai - gne de tout dan-ger
While I in dan- ger be,
Tou-jours, tou-jours la
Her life, keep Thou from

pro - té ger, Cet - te soeur si ché-
dan - ger free, Keep her soul in its per-
ri e, Dai - gne de tout dan-
fec tion! While I in dan- ger
ger la pro - té - ger, Dai - gne la pro - té -
be, I pray of Thee, O keep her soul of
ger de tout dan - ger.
mor- tal dan- ger free!

SERENADE

FROM FAUST

BY CHARLES GOUNOD

LIBRETTO BY JULES BARBIER AND MICHEL CARRÉ

First performance at Théâtre Lyrique, Paris, March 19, 1859

While Valentin was off to the wars, Faust, under the tutelage of Méphistophélès, seduced Valentin's sister Marguerite. With Valentin back in town (having returned to the accompaniment of the familiar *Soldiers' Chorus*), Méphistophélès takes the opportunity to sing this mocking and insulting serenade before the family house. (The name of the family, by the way, though it is mentioned nowhere in the opera, was Oppenheim.) Faust looks on uncomfortably as Méphistophélès sings and accompanies himself on the guitar. The result of this escapade is that Valentin storms furiously out of the house, challenges Faust to a duel, and is slain when the devil, acting as referee, directs Faust's sword to a fatal spot.

The serenade presents the basso with a splendid chance to mug or to show off his real acting and interpretive ability. The final ha-ha-has, on three different Gs, are also a cruel challenge to his range, and many is the basso who diplomatically concludes that it is more dramatic (and safer) to cover the high or the low G with fiendish laughter.

Allegretto
f
f
poco meno mosso
p
p sub.
Vous qui faî - tes l'en-dor -
You be - hind your win - dow
mi - e, N'en- ten - dez- vous pas, N'en-ten - dez - vous pas,
sleep - ing, My be - lov - ed Kate, Chaste and love- ly Kate,
Ô Ca - the - ri - ne, ma mi - e, N'en-ten-dez-vous pas, Ma voix et mes
All my life is in your keep-ing; Can you hear me, Kate? Can you let me
3

pas?
wait?
Ain - si ton ga - lant t'ap - pel - le,
Thus your gal - lant se - re - nades you;
rit.
Ain - si ton ga - lant t'ap - pel - le,
Thus you wake and he per - suades you
Et ton coeur l'en
To most an - y -
rit.
a tempo
croit. Ah! Ah! Ah! ah! ah! ah! ah! ah! ah! ah!
thing! Ha! Ha! Ha! Ha! Ha! Ha! Ha! Ha! Ha! Ha!
N'ou-vre ta por - te, ma bel - le
Lock the door and don't be - lieve him
Que la bague au
'til you wear his

doigt, N'ou — vre ta por - te, ma bel - le, Que la bague au
ring! Well — be - low your win - dow leave him 'til you wear his
cresc.
doigt, Que la bague au doigt Ah! ah! ah! ah! ah! ah! ah! ah! ah!
ring, 'til you wear his ring! Ha! Ha! Ha! Ha! Ha! Ha! Ha! Ha! Ha!
f
rit.
ah! ah! ah! ah! ah!
Ha! Ha! Ha! Ha! Ha!
Presto
ff

JEWEL SONG

FROM FAUST

BY CHARLES GOUNOD

LIBRETTO BY JULES BARBIER AND MICHEL CARRÉ

First performance at Théâtre Lyrique, Paris, March 19, 1859

The "Garden Scene" (Act II) of *Faust* begins with Marguerite's young lover, Siebel, gathering a bouquet of flowers and leaving them on her doorstep as a message of love. When Méphistophélès sees them, he provides his protégé, Faust, with a far more resplendent offering—a casket of jewels, complete with mirror. A little later Marguerite discovers Siebel's pretty but inexpensive gift, only to have it fade into insignificance beside the devilish attractions of costume jewelry.

She adorns herself and admires herself as she sings the *Jewel Song*—the only passage in the entire role where the soprano is called upon to employ scales, trills, and other ordnance from the armory of the coloratura.

Allegretto
Original in E
p leggiero
cresc.
dim.
Ah! Je ris
Ah! what joy
f
dim.
pp
de me voir si belle en ce mi - roir, Ah! je ris
to ap - pear so love - ly in the glass! Ah! I know
de me voir si belle en ce mi - roir, Est - ce
ne - ver has it shown me such a lass! Gret - chen,
cresc.

3

toi, Mar - gue - ri - te, Est - ce toi?
is it real - ly you, then? Can it be?
Ré-ponds-moi, ré-ponds-moi, ré-ponds, ré-ponds, ré-ponds vi - te!
An-swer me! Im-age dear, is your fair re-flec-tion true, then?
cresc.
dim.
Non! non! Ce n'est pas toi! Non!
No, no! I am much less! No,
non, ce n'est plus ton vi - sa - ge: C'est la
no, you can - not be my im - age But a

fil — le d'un roi, C'est la
high — born prin — cess, But a
fil — le d'un roi! Ce n'est plus toi,
high — born prin — cess! I am much less.
cresc.
Ce n'est plus toi, C'est la fil - le d'un roi, Qu'on sa -
You are not me But a no - ble prin - cess All bow
f
lue au pas - sa - ge! Ah, s'il é - tait i - ci!
down to in ho - mage! Ah! were he here with me!
p

rit.
a tempo
S'il me voy - ait ain - si! Comme u-ne de-moi - sel - le
If he could on-ly see What dig-ni-ty these lend me,
pp
Il me trou-ve-rait bel - le, Ah!
How love-ly he would find me! Ah!
cresc.
Comme u-ne de-moi-selle il me trou-ve-rait bel - le Comme u-ne de-moi-
Could he but see me now, would he not find me love - ly! Could he but see me
f
rit.
a tempo
selle Il me trou-ve-rait bel - le! Mar - gue
now, Would he not find me love - ly! Love - ly
colla voce
p a tempo
cresc.
pp

ri - te, Ce n'est plus toi! Ce n'est plus ton vi -
im - age, you are not me! You can - not be my
sempre cresc.
f
sa — ge! Non! C'est la fil - le d'un
im — age, No! You're a no - ble prin -
f
roi, — Qu'on sa - lue au pas - sa —
cess! — All bow down to in ho —
f
— ge!
— mage!
Vivo
ff
8va

VESTI LA GIUBBA

FROM PAGLIACCI

BY RUGGIERO LEONCAVALLO

LIBRETTO BY THE COMPOSER

First performance at Teatro dal Verme, Milan, May 21, 1892

Tonio, as an act of vengeance, brings back his master from the village tavern in time to overhear Nedda planning to elope with her local lover, Silvio. He chases after Silvio, but finds no trace of him. In a rage, he threatens his wife, but another member of the troupe takes away his knife and reminds him that he must prepare for the evening performance. Canio closes Act I with this most famous aria, the classic expression of the laugh-clown-laugh agony.

At the performance that evening Canio improvises a tragic ending to the comedy being performed, by murdering both his wife and her lover. In the real-life story on which Leoncavallo based his opera the murder was singular and less dramatically apt. The actor, named Alessandro, murdered his wife after the play was over, and the lover got away alive.

Adagio
con dolore
Original in E minor
p
Ve - sti la giub - ba e la fac - cia in - fa - ri - na.
Put on the mot - ley and the grease-paint for cov - er,
p
portando
La gen - te pa - ga e ri - der vuo - le qua.
It is for laugh - ter the pub - lic will have paid.
E se Ar - lec - chin t'in - vo - la Co - lom - bi - na,
Should Col - um - bine make Har - le - quin her lov - er,
violento
ri - di, Pa - gliac - cio e o - gnun ap - plau - di - rà!
Laugh, laugh, Pa - gliac - cio! They'll cheer the mas - quer - ade!
8va

poco rit.
a tempo
Tra-mu-ta in laz-zi lo spa-smo ed il pian-to;
Trans-form each tear of your life that has mat-tered
col canto
a tempo
8va
string.
cresc. rit.
in u-na smor-fia il sin-ghioz-zo e'l do-lor Ah!
In-to some rau-cous gri-mac-es of your art, Ah!
col canto
cresc. rit.
8va
full voice (breaking)
espress.
Ri-di, Pa-gliac-cio, sul tuo a-mo-re in-fran-to! Ri-di del
Laugh, laugh Pa-gliac-cio, when your love has been shat-tered, Laugh while you
f molto rit.
yielding
duol che t'av-ve-le-na il cor!
die hid-ing what poi-sons your heart!
col canto
mf espr.

BALLATELLA

FROM PAGLIACCI

BY RUGGIERO LEONCAVALLO

LIBRETTO BY THE COMPOSER

First performance at Teatro dal Verme, Milan, May 21, 1892

In Act I of *Pagliacci,* Canio, leader of a troupe of traveling actors, has expressed, in no uncertain terms, his readiness to avenge himself on anyone who finds his pretty young wife and leading lady too attractive to keep his hands to himself.

Left alone, this girl, Nedda, shakes off the depression induced by Canio's threats, and then sings the *Ballatella.* It is a paean to the aimless freedom that birds seem to have. Perhaps there is a significance to the fact that she makes only the briefest reference, in a recitative preceding the aria, to the lover she has in the town the troupe has just entered and with whom she soon plans to elope. It is just aimless freedom the girl wishes for, like the birds'.

While she is singing, Tonio, the hunchbacked low comedian of the troupe, slinks in and, when she is through, mockingly applauds. He thereupon tries, with notable lack of success, to force his own attentions on her.

Vivace (steady tempo)
Original in F# Major
p
Stri — do — no las — sù, — li — be — ra — men — te lan - cia - ti a vol, — a vol co - me frec - ce, glian -
Light with song they go — cease — less — ly, free — ly; Swift - ly in flight — in flight they go ev - er more
8va
Legato
pp
cantando

gel. Di sfi da no le nu
high! Our shad ows they dis dain
8va
bi e'l sol co cen te, e
and our wing less yearn ing, Through
con anima
8va
van ne e van no per le vie del
lanes more op en can their yearn ing
8va
mf Slightly broader
ciel. La scia
fly ! Through lanes
8va

returning to tempo
te - li va - gar per l'at mo -
ev - er more wide what makes them
8va
col canto
sfe ra, que sti as se ta
wan der? Why on - ward to hea
8va
ti d'az - zur - ro e di splen - dor:
ven et er - nal - ly must they soar?
8va
Se guo no, an - ch'es si un so gno
Are they as well drawn by bright and
8va

84

u - na chi - me - ra, e van - no, e
van - ish - ing vis - ions? They fly still
8va
van - no fra le nu - bi d'or!
high - er and shall fly still more
loco
animando
Che in - cal - zi il ven - to e la - tri
! On through the tem - pest, the heav - en
la - tem - pe - sta con l'a - li a - per
shak - ing thun - der, On through the light
cresc.

f
te — san tut - to sfi - dar; — la piog - gia, i
ning with wings op - en wide — ! Past fire and
f
lam - pi, nul - la mai li ar - re — sta, e
gla - cier, ov - er peak and oc — ean, They
van - no e van — no su - gli a - bis — sie i mar. —
fly still on — ward with un - brok — en pride! —
con anima
Van — no lag -
Ev — er in
cantando

giù ver so un pa e se stra
song they seek a hid den king
no che so gnan for se e che
dom, They seek in vain, yet they
cer ca no in van.
seek till they die.
Mai bo
But their
ë mi del ciel
joy is in flight,
poco rit.
Se guon l'ar
Though what they

a tempo
ca no po - ter che li so - spin
dream Can - not be; though it be noth
a tempo
ge... e van! e van! e
ing, they fly! they fly! they
Presto
f
van! e van!
fly! they fly!
8va
f
8va
8va
col canto
sec

VOI LO SAPETE

FROM CAVALLERIA RUSTICANA

BY PIETRO MASCAGNI

LIBRETTO BY GIOVANNI TARGIONI-TOZZETTI AND GUIDO MENASCI

First performance at Teatro Constanzi, Rome, May 17, 1890

On Easter morning in a Sicilian village, a fine hymn has been sung by double chorus and soprano solo just before the services. Santuzza, the heroine of the opera, however, does not dare enter the church with the others, for she has been betrayed by her lover, Turiddu, who promised before he left for military service to marry her but is now carrying on an affair with a young married woman. Santuzza detains Lucia, Turiddu's mother, as she is about to enter the church and brokenheartedly utters her complaints in this aria. She gets no comfort from the older woman, who shuffles off into the church.

Original in E Minor
Voi lo sa - pe - te, O mam-ma pri-ma d'an-dar sol - da - to Tu-
You must have known, O ma—ma, Lo - la and your Tu - rid - du, Be-
rid - du a - ve - vaa Lo - la e—— ter - na fè giu - ra - to, a-
fore his year as a sol - dier, found—— that they loved each oth - er And
ve - va a Lo - la e - ter - na fè giu—ra——— to.—— Tor-
vowed they would be true to love for—e——— ver.—— He

nò la sep-pe spo — sa; e con un nuo-vo a-mo — re —
left; Lo-la soon mar — ried. When he came back, her lo — ver —
cresc.
vol-le spe gner la fiam-ma che gli bru-cia-va il co-re
tried for-get-ting his heart-break, mak-ing love to an-oth-er
poco rit.
a tempo
animando
piu f
rit.
ff
m'a-mò — L'a-ma-i, l'a-ma-i ah! —
To me! — He loved me. I loved him. God! —
sentito
accel poco a poco
con grande passione
a tempo
l'a-ma-i
I love him!
affrettando
grandioso appassionato
poco rit.

pp
Quell' in - vi - da
When Lo - la saw
dim.
pp legatiss
d'o-gni de - li - zia mi - a
she was no long - er need - ed,
del suo spo - so di-
Mar - riage vows were no
men - ti - ca,
bar to her;
ar - se di ge - lo - si - a
shame - less - ly she pur - sued him
ar - se di ge - lo-
Jea - lous that I was
f rit.
si - a,
hap - py
Me l'ha ra - pi — to,
and she suc - cee — ded!
me l'ha ra-
She stole Tu-
rit.
ff

p
pi - to.
rid - du!
Pri - va dell' o - nor
More than ev - er I
p
piu f
cresc. e animando
mi — o dell' o - nor mi - o ri - man - go: Lo - la e Tu - rid - du
need him, He who has ta - ken my ho - nor! Now I've been thrown a -
più f
cresc. e animando
s'a - ma - no, Lo - la e Tu - rid - du s'a - ma - no, io — pian
way by him; Lo - la's be - come his love a - gain; I — weep a -
ff
—go, io pian — go, io pian — go!
lone, I weep a - lone, a - lone I weep!
8va

LE RÊVE

FROM MANON

BY JULES MASSENET

LIBRETTO BY HENRI MEILHAC AND PHILIPPE GILLE

First performance at Opéra-Comique, Paris, January 19, 1884

A glance at the words to which this quietly passionate aria is set shows them to express the traditional dream of the romantic but impecunious lover—a simple house in the country surrounded by nothing but good weather. The situation in which Des Grieux utters his conventional lyric is, however, full of dramatic irony. The young nobleman does not know that a few minutes earlier his beloved Manon, who had eloped with him while she was en route to school, has connived at his abduction by his father so that she may be free to become the mistress of a wealthy roué. In her sentimental duplicity she has already bidden a touching farewell to her first home away from home, singing *Adieu, notre petite table,* a quiet little aria not less affecting than *Le rêve* because less sincere.

Andante très calme
Des Grieux:
En fer-mant les yeux je vois Là-
In the realm of dream I stood And
Andante très calme
pp very softly and sustained
espr.
bas une hum-ble re-trai-te U-ne mai-son
saw a mod-est a-bode there; By it-self it
poco
net-te Tou-te blanche au fond des bois!
glowed there White-ly through a sec-ret wood.
dolce
poco
Sous ses tran-quil-les om-bra-ges Les
And through the calm of that sha-dow The
poco

clairs et joy-eux ruis-seaux, Où se mi-rent les feuil-
hap-py sound of clear streams Thread-ing to a sun-lit
p
dolce
poco rall.
rall. ten.
a tempo
la ges, Chan-tent a-vec les oi-seaux!
mea dow, Joined the lark's cel-es-tial themes
suivez
sf
C'est le pa-ra-dis! Oh! non tout est
It was E-den there! Yet, no! All was
f espr.
là triste et mo-ro se, Car il y manque u-ne
mourn-ful there and lone some. One want a-lone made it
dim
f
espr.

Manon:
dolce
C'est un rêve, u - ne fo-
You were dream-ing, lost in il-
(Des Grieux:)
rall. dim.
chose il y faut en-core Ma - non!
so I did not see you, Ma - non!
pp
(Manon:)
li - e!
lu - sion.
sf
(Des G.:)
Non! Là se - ra no - tre vi - e, Si tu le
No! That could be our se - clu - sion If you'd con -
sf
dim.
veux, ô Ma - non!
sent O Ma - non!
f
pp
pp
poco
r.h.
Ped. * Ped. * Ped. *

O PARADISO!

FROM L'AFRICAINE

BY GIACOMO MEYERBEER

LIBRETTO BY EUGÈNE SCRIBE

First performance at Grand Opéra, Paris, April 28, 1865

Vasco da Gama, the Portuguese explorer who was the first to find a way to India by sailing around Africa, is the hero of this opera and the singer of the aria. His intrepidity is exemplified by the text, as well as his susceptibilities to natural beauty. In the fourth act the ship on which he has been a captive has been burned by Indians, the female passengers have just been condemned to death, screaming, offstage, and he has been led by soldiers before a temple where he is to meet a similar fate. Yet, so deeply is he impressed by the luxuriant natural growth about him that he thinks himself in an earthly paradise, and expresses his desire for the place with all the ardor he might have reserved for either of the two beautiful heroines of the story, Inez and Selika.

The original language of this pseudo-historical opera is French. Yet, because the Metropolitan Opera Company used to perform it in Italian, and because Caruso's recording of this aria was one of his most popular, most Americans think of the name of the opera as *L'Africana* and the name of the aria as *O Paradiso!*

Andantino
Recit. a tempo
p
Pa - ys mer-veil-leux,
Mir - a - cle of realms,
p
dolce sostenuto
8va
jar - dins for - tu - nés,
tem-ple of de-light,
Tem-ple ra - di - eux, sa -
Gar - den of the blest, all
lut!
hail!
dolce
O Pa - ra - dis, sor - ti de
O Vis-ion of Ed - en from deeps up
poco rall.
8va
l'on - de, Ciel si bleu ciel si pur dont mes yeux sont ra -
lift - ed, Shin - ing mount, shad - owed vale That has ra - vished my
cresc.

molto
vis, Tu m'ap - par - tiens, Ô nou - veau mon de, Dont j'au - rai do - té, dont j'au - rai do - té mon pa-
sight! My heart is yours, New world of won der That I long to take, That I long to take for my
p
cresc.
un poco rit.
8va

a tempo
con calore
ys.
own!
À nous_ ces cam-pagnes_ ver-
To claim_ what is hea - ven
mf
p
meilles
gift-ed!
A nous_ cet E - den re-trou-vé!
To con-quer where strife is un-known!
dolce
Ô_ tre-sors char-mants,
O_ in-spi-ring charm,
Ô_ mer-veil-les,
life_ un-dreamed of,
sa-
To
cantabile
lut!
you!
Mon-de Nou-veau,
Re-cov-ered world,
tu m'ap-par-
un-sul-lied
con
fp

entusiasmo
tiens, sois done à moi,
love, You have my heart!
à moi, sois donc à moi, ô beau pa-
Di - vine Un - troub - led land, you shall be
poco rall.
f
dim.
segue
f con calore
ys. Mon-de non-veau, tum'ap-par-tiens; sois donc à moi, sois donc à moi, à
mine! O ra-diant land, un-troub-led realm, You shall be mine, You shall be mine, be
moi, à moi!
mine, my own!
f
p
a tempo

LÀ CI DAREM LA MANO

FROM DON GIOVANNI

BY WOLFGANG AMADEUS MOZART

LIBRETTO BY LORENZO DA PONTE

First performance at National Theater, Prague, October 29, 1787

This superficially simple, almost childlike, duet is a superbly subtle example of one aspect of Mozart's genius—his ability to characterize human beings and their actions through writing notes. In the first scene of the opera the Don has made love to one aristocratic lady and slain her father; in the second scene he has escaped from the attentions of a former mistress and turned her over to his servant. Now, in the third scene, he comes across a pretty peasant celebrating her betrothal to her village swain, and he begins still another conquest. This time, however, his style is utterly changed: he speaks in accents simple, direct, sweet, yet aristocratic and reassuring. He invites the girl merely to take his hand and walk "over there" ("there" being an arbor on the stage). And when she archly replies, taking up his own tune, he becomes just a little more pressing, overcoming her faint scruples about Masetto, her fiancé. Once that is done, the time picks up, the rhythm becomes more urgent, changing from 2/4 to 6/8, and the two voices are joined. But even as they approach the arbor, they still protest that their love is *innocènte*—an Italian word that means (not very surprisingly) "innocent."

At the première of the opera, which Mozart himself conducted, this duet had to be repeated three times. After that, encores were forbidden.

Andante
Don Giovanni:
Là ci da-rem la ma-no, là mi di-rai di
Dal-ly your hand in my hand, Let our de-signs a-
sì ve-di, non è lon-ta-no, par
gree. Lin-ger-ing here serves no one; Why
tiam, ben mio, da qui.
not walk on with me?
Zerlina:
Vor-rei, e non vo-
My heart is more than
re-i, mi trem-a un po-co il cor, fe-
will-ing: I trem-ble to de-part. Yet

li - ce, è ver, sa - re - i, ma può bur - lar - mi an
fear you may de - ceive me should I ob - ey my
cor, ma può bur - lar mi an - cor!
heart. Should I ob - ey my heart?
Don Giovanni:
Zer.:
Vie - ni, mio bel di - let - to! Mi fa pie - tà Ma -
Come to your no - ble lov - er! Must poor Ma - set - to
mf
p
Don Giovanni:
Zer.:
set - to! Io can - gie - rò tuo sor - te! Pre -
suf - fer? Pea - sant you'll be no lon - ger! Faint -
p

sto non son più for - te, non son più
ly I would that I were strong - er, I would that I were
Don G.:
for - te, non son più for - te! Vie - ni vie - ni!
strong - er, I would that I were strong - er! Dear - est, gent - ly
sf p
Zer.:
Là ci da - rem la ma - no Vor - rei, e non vor - re - i,
Dal - ly your hand in my hand! I fear you may de - ceive me.
Don G.:
Zer.:
Là mi di - rai di sì, Mi tre - ma un po - co il
Why not walk on with me? I trem - ble to de
p

Zer.:
cor; ma può bur - lar mi an
part. Should I ob - ey my
Don G.:
par-tiam, ben mio, da qui.
Let our de - signs a - gree!
cor. Mi fa pie - ta Ma - set - to; pre
heart? Must poor Ma - set - to suf - fer? Dear
Vie - ni, mio bel di - let - to! io can - gie - ro tuo
Come to your no - ble lov - er! Pea - sant you'll be no
mf
p
mf
p
sto non son più for - te, non son più for - te, non son più
ly I hope I can be strong - er, I hope I can be strong - er, I hope I can be
sor - te!
lon - ger!
p

for — te!
An - diam! I will!
An - diam! My love!
An - diam! Be mine!
Allegro
An - diam, an - diam, mio be - ne, a ri — sto - rar le
To - geth — er let us pure - ly In - dulge a whim we
An - diam, an - diam, mio be - ne, a ri — sto - rar le
To - geth - er let us pure - ly in - dulge a whim we
Allegro
pe - ne d'un' in — no — cen — te a -
sure - ly Are fault — less to ful -
pe - ne d'un' in — no — cen — te a -
sure - ly Are fault — less to ful -

p
mor! Andiam, andiam, mio
fill! For noble man and
mor! Andiam, andiam, mio
fill! For noble man and
bene a ri storar le pene d'un'
peasant While doing what is pleasant, Can-
bene a ri storar le pene d'un'
peasant While doing what is pleasant, Can-
in no cen te a mor!
not be doing ill!
in no cen te a mor!
not be doing ill!
p

An -
Hold
An diam!
Dear est!
diam!
me!
An diam!
Love me!
An - diam, mio be - ne, an-
We'll go with-out de -
An - diam!
I will
An - diam, mio be - ne, an-
We'll go with-out de -

diam! le pe - ne a ri - sto - rar d'un
lay And cheer - ful - ly at play, Love
diam! le pe - ne a ri - sto - rar d'un
lay And cheer - ful - ly at play, Love
in — no — cen — te a - mor!
in — no — cent — ly still!
in — no - cen — te a - mor!
in — no - cent — ly still!

IL MIO TESORO

FROM DON GIOVANNI

BY WOLFGANG AMADEUS MOZART

LIBRETTO BY LORENZO DA PONTE

First performance at National Theater, Prague, October 29, 1787

It has been remarked more than once that the baritone villain in almost any given opera is a more colorful character than the tenor hero. Perhaps this is nowhere truer than in *Don Giovanni,* in which the name role is the most fascinating of baritone evildoers while Don Ottavio is the most ineffectual of tenor characters. He comes on stage first to console his fiancée over her father's dead body; he promises to do whatever he can to help her; and all he can think of—shortly before this aria is sung in the second scene of Act II—is that maybe he had better call in the police. Yet so sincere are the accents in which he wishes someone or something to console Donna Anna for him that he wins our complete sympathy. And when he swears personal vengeance in the middle, and very difficult, section of the aria, one is all but convinced that a man who can express himself in such noble scale passages must, sooner or later, act like a hero. Alas, he never does.

Andante
Il mio te - so — ro in - tan — to
Fly, gen-tle notes to — aid her;
an — da — te, an — da —
Sweet mu — sic As my her —
— te a — con — so — lar!
— aid — swift — ly — fly!
e del bel ci - glio il
Go to — my — love, per -
pian — to cer — ca — te — di a — sciu —
suade — her Those flow — ing — tears to —

gar, cer - ca te cer - ca te, cer -
dry: Sweet mu - sic at - tend her Of
ca te dia sciu - gar, cer -
whom your grace is born: Con -
ca
sole
te dia - sciu - gar.
her! Fly, O fly!
1.

Di — te - le che i suoi tor ti a ven - di - car io
Say she is not for - sak - en, Ev — er shall I de -
va — do, a — ven - di - car — io —
fend her, Ev — en till death, — de —
f
va - do che sol di stra — gie
fend her! My sol — emn vow is
fp
p
mor — ti Nun — zio — vo - gl'io tor -
tak — en Ne — ver — to — be for -
fp
p
p

nar nun zio vogl' io tor nar, si,
sworn! soon shall her wrong-er die! Yes!
cresc.
p
cresc.
nun zio vogl'io tor nar!
Soon shall her wrong er die!
f
p
2.
gar.
Fly!
f
Da capo
116

NON PIÙ ANDRAI

FROM LE NOZZE DI FIGARO

BY WOLFGANG AMADEUS MOZART

LIBRETTO BY LORENZO DA PONTE

First performance at Burgtheater, Vienna, May 1, 1786

One of the most engaging characters in all of opera is Cherubino, a page in the court of Count Almaviva. He is so much delighted with the idea of being in love that he flirts with every reasonably youthful female in the cast, from the Countess herself to the gardener's daughter. This propensity has got him into so much trouble that by the end of Act I, the Count has decided to get rid of him by commissioning him as an ensign and ordering him to join up at once. Among those who consider this a good riddance is Figaro, and he closes the act by singing him this mock-military tune while marching him up and down the room. Fortunately, for all lovers of fine music and fine comedy, Cherubino does not at once obey his master but remains prominently on stage and in trouble for the rest of the opera.

Vivace
Figaro:
Non più an-drai, far-fal-lo ne a-mo-
You will not have the time now to
ro so not-te e gior no d'in-tor no gi-
flit ter Flash-ing love's in-dis-crim-in-ate
ran do, del le bel le tur ban do il ri-
glit ter; In a man's world you'll find it were
po so, Nar ci-set to A-don-ci no d'a-
fit ter Play ing beard less A-don is no

mor, del — le bel — le tur — ban — do il ri —
more, In a man's world you'll find it were
po — so, Nar — ci — set — to A - don - ci — no d'a —
fit - ter Play - ing beard — less A - don — is no
mf
p
mor.
more.
f
5
5
non più a — vrai que - sti bei pen - nac -
Sweep — ing plumes of a gal — lant per -
p

chi ni,
fec tion,
quel cap
Bright a
f
p
pel lo leg - ge roe gal - lan te,
ban don and ten der af - fec tion,
quel - la
That ver -
chio ma quell' a ria bril - lan te
mil lion un - man ly com - plex ion,
quel ver -
You can
mi glio don - ne sco co - lor
hard ly main-tain as be - fore,
quel ver -
You can
cresc.

mi — glio don-ne - sco co - lor! Non più a
hard — ly main-tain as be - fore: Now no
vrai quei pen-nac-chi - ni, quel cap-
more, af-fec-tion ten-der, bright a-
pel - lo, quel-la chio-ma, quell' a — ria bril-
ban - don, That ver-mil - lion un - man — ly com-
lan - te! Non più an-drai, far - fal - lo — ne a - mo-
plex - ion! Mai - den arms will pro-vide you no
f
p
cresc.
f
p

ro — so, not - te e gior — no d'in-tor — no gi-
har — bor, pret - ty ring — lets a - dorn you no
ran — do, del — le bel — le tur - ban - do il ri-
long — ger: To the world, to cam-paigns, to the
po — so, Nar — ci - set — to, A - don - ci — no d'a-
bar — ber You must march with dis-patch through the
mp
mor, del — le bel — le tur - ban - do il ri-
door, To the world, to cam-paigns, to the

po — so, Nar — ci - set — to, A - don - ci — no d'a-
bar — ber You must march with dis-patch through the
mor. Che - ru — bi - no al - la it—
door! Che - ru — bi - no, now be
to — ria, al - la glo - ria mi — li—
strong - er! On to man-hood! On to
tar, Che — rub - bi — no, al-la vit -
war! Che — rub - bi — no, now be
23

to - ria, al la glo ria, mi li -
strong - er! On to man hood! On to
tar, al la glo ria mi li -
war! On to man hood! On to
tar, al la glo ria mi li -
war! On to vic tor - y at
tar!
war!
f

VOI CHE SAPETE

FROM LE NOZZE DI FIGARO

BY WOLFGANG AMADEUS MOZART

LIBRETTO BY LORENZO DA PONTE

First performance at Burgtheater, Vienna, May 1, 1786

Cherubino, the page, has composed the words and music of a song for his beloved young countess, and in the first scene of Act II he shyly presents it to her and, only after some urging, sings it as the maid in waiting, Susanna, accompanies him on the guitar. Earlier in the opera the boy (so young that his part is written for a soprano) had frankly confided his love for the countess to Susanna and poured out his excitement in a swift, uninhibited aria, *Non so più cosa son.* Now, however, he is modestly contained, and, in quite general terms, asks, "Can this really be love?" The mounting strength of his feeling is quietly and beautifully suggested as each succeeding measure rises to a higher note, while the fluttering of his heart may be suspected from the little staccato descending scales that occur now and then in the accompaniment.

Yet, quite regardless of the subtle psychological comments that the shape of the aria makes on Cherubino, the melody, in absolute terms, is one of the loveliest ever penned by even a Mozart.

Andante con moto
Cherubino:
p
Voi, che sa - pe te che co sa è a -
You that know clear ly What love may be when
p
mor, Don ne, ve de te,
real Is it sin cere ly
s'io l'ho nel cor, Don ne ve -
Love that I feel, Is it sin -
de te, s'io l'ho nel cor.
cere ly Love that I feel?

Quel - lo ch'io pro — vo, vi — ri - di - rò —
Feel - ings, my la — dies, Strange - ly so new, —
È per me nuo — vo ca — pir nol so
Beg - ging your aid — is All — I can do.
sen - to un af — fet — to pien di de - sir, —
Sim - ple de — sir — ing Leaves me per - plexed,
Ch'o - ra è di - let — to, ch'o - ra è mar - tir.
One mo-ment in — spi — ring, Rack - ing the next.

Ge — lo, e poi sen — to l'al - ma‿av-vam - par,
Freez — ing and fev — er Hold_ me in turn:
E in un mo - men — to — tor — no a ge-lar.
Ar - den - tly I shi — ver, — I — ci - ly I burn.
Ri — cer - co un be — ne fuo — ri di me,
I seek a me — rit Not of my own,
r.h.
l.h.
Non so chi il tie — ne, non so cos'
Dear to in — her — it, Mine, yet un -

è. So - spi - ro e ge - mo sen - za vo - ler Pal - pi - to e
known. Though hap - py liv - ing, I sob and sigh Faint with mis -
fp
tre - mo sen - za sa - per. Non tro - vo pa - ce not - te nè
giv - ing, And know not why; Nor why this ver - nal Lack of all
fp
dì, ma pur mi pia — ce lan — guir co -
ease, This pang et — er — nal So much can
sì. Voi che sa - pe - te che co - sa e a -
please. You that know clear - ly What love may be when

mor, Don - ne, ve - de - te, s'io l'ho nel
real, Is it sin-cere - ly Love that I
cor, Don - ne ve - de - te, s'io l'ho nel
feel? Is it sin - cere - ly Love that I
cor, Don ne, ve - de te,
feel? Is it sin - cere ly
s'io l'ho nel cor.
Love that I feel?

O ISIS UND OSIRIS

FROM DIE ZAUBERFLÖTE

BY WOLFGANG AMADEUS MOZART

LIBRETTO BY EMANUEL SCHIKANEDER AND JOHANN GEORG METZLER (GIESECKE)

First performance at Theater auf der Wieden, Vienna, September 30, 1791

Most of the second of *The Magic Flute's* two acts is devoted to the preparation and tests for admission to the Temple of Light of two aristocratic characters, Pamina and Tamino, and one peasant, Papageno. The Temple of Light is presided over by Sarastro, the high priest of the Egyptian gods Isis and Osiris. Sarastro seems to direct the tests and to make the rules, and admission and its ceremonies seem to be based on analogous procedures in the lodges of the Freemasons, of whom Mozart was a member.

At the opening of Act II, Sarastro presides over a meeting of the priests of the temple, informs them that Pamina and Tamino are intended for each other, orders them brought to the temple porch, and then intones this solemn and profoundly dignified melody, a blessing upon the novitiates.

"It is the only music," wrote George Bernard Shaw, "which might be put into the mouth of God without blasphemy."

Adagio
Sarastro: p
O I - sis und O - si - ris
O I - sis and O - si - ris
schen - ket der Weis - heit Geist dem neu - en Paar! Die ihr der
hear him, Ac - cept this vow that he has made, In hours of
Wand' rer Schrit - te len - ket, stärkt mit Ge - duld sie - in Ge - fahr,
tri - al and grief be near him, Com - fort his heart when sore a - fraid,
Priests: p
stärkt mit Ge - duld sie in Ge - fahr Stärkt mit Ge - duld sie in Ge-
And guide him through the dread - ful shade And guide him through the dread - ful

Sarastro:
fahr. Lasst sie der Prü - fung Früch-te se - hen doch sol - len sie zu
shade. May love be born of_ tri - bu - la-tion, Show him the path to
Gra - be ge - hen so lohnt der Tu - gend küh - nen Lauf, nehmt sie in
his sal - va - tion, And when this mor - tal life__shall cease, From vain de -
eu - ren Wohn-sitz auf,__ nehmt sie in eu - ren Wohn-sitz auf,
sire the soul re - lease,- Grant him your ev - er - last - ing peace.
Priests:
p
nehmt sie in eu - ren Wohn-sitz auf.
Grant him your ev - er - last - ing peace.

BARCAROLLE

FROM LES CONTES D'HOFFMANN

BY JACQUES OFFENBACH

LIBRETTO BY JULES BARBIER AND MICHEL CARRÉ

First performance at Opéra-Comique, Paris, February 10, 1881

The second of the three tales of the poet Hoffmann rehearsed in this opera concerns the perfidy of a Venetian courtesan named Giulietta. The episode takes place at an evening party in her palatial home on one of the canals, and it opens as she sings the *Barcarolle* with Hoffmann's constant companion, a worldly-wise youth named Nicklausse, whose part is written for a mezzo-soprano. The gently undulating rhythm and melody seem ideally suited to set the stage for the water-borne tragedy of sex and avarice that is to follow; and the same melody is used at the close of the episode with great dramatic effect as a fatal duel is fought between two of Giulietta's lovers while she floats away in a gondola, laughing in the arms of a third.

It comes as a bit of a surprise, then, to discover that this music, which seems to represent the very spirit of tawdry Venetian romance and tragedy, was originally composed by Offenbach seventeen years earlier for a Viennese operetta called *Die Rheinnixen,* or *The Mermaids of the Rhine.* In this operetta the name of the tune was *The Goblin Song.*

Nicklausse:
p
Bel- le nuit ô nuit d'a-mour, Sou-
Love-ly night, O bound-less night, En-
pp
Ped. * Ped. * Ped. * Ped. *
ris_ à nos i— vres— ses! Nuit plus dou- ce que_ le jour, ô
chant, ca- ress and co— ver! Trem-bling gar-den of de-light, O
simile
Giulietta:
p
Le temps fuit et sans re- tour Em-
Time will car- ry in his flight The
Nick:
bel- le nuit d'a- mour! Le temps fuit et sans re- tour Em-
bound-less love- ly night!
senza arpegg.

por— te nos ten— dres— ses Loin de cet heu- reux sé- jour Le
loved one and the lov—— er; In your spell we stay in spite of
por— te nos ten- dres— ses Loin de cet heu- reux sé- jour Le
temps fuit sans re— tour.—— Zé-phirs— em-bra— ses
times re— lent— less flight!—— With love— we em— bark
temps fuit sans re- tour.——
Zé- phirs— em- bra-
With love— we em-
— Ver-sez-nous vos ca-res- ses, Zé- phirs— em- bra- sés
— We em-brace and we hov- er; With love— we em- bark
sés Ver— sez-nous Ver-sez-nous vos ca-
bark, We— em-brace Em-brac-ing we shall

Don-nez-nous vos bai-sers, Vos bai-sers!
Ov-er seas of the dark, on the dark,
res-ses, vos bai-sers! Ver-sez-nous, Ver-sez-
hov-er on the dark! We em-brace Ov-er
Ped. * Ped. *
vos bai-sers! Ah!
on the dark! Ah!
(with chorus humming)
Bel- le nuit! ô
Love-ly night, O
nous vos bai-sers! Ah!
seas of the dark! Ah!
Bel- le nuit! ô
pp
Ped. * Ped. * Ped. *
nuit d'a-mour, Sou-ris à nos i-vres-ses, Nuit plus dou-ce
bound-less night, En-chant, ca-ress and cov-er; Trem-bling gar-den
nuit d'a-mour, Sou-ris à nos i-vres-ses, Nuit plus dou-ce
pp
Ped. * Ped. * Ped. * Ped. *

sf
que le jour, Ô bel-le nuit d'a-mour!
of de-light, O bound-less love-ly night!
sf
que le jour, Ô bel-le nuit d'a-mour!
Ô bel-le nuit d'a-
O with love we em-
Ped. * Ped. *
f
Ah! Sou-ris à nos i-vres-ses! Nuit d'a-
Ah! We em-brace and we hov-er on the
f
mour!
bark!
Sou-ris à nos i-vres-ses!
We em-brace and we hov-er
f
dim.
pp
mour ô nuit d'a-mour! Ah! ah!
bound-less love-ly dark! Ah! ah!
pp
Ô bel-le nuit d'a-mour! ah!
ov-er the seas of the dark! ah!
pp

ppp
ah! ah! ah!
ppp
ah! ah! ah!
dim.
ah! ah! ah!
ah! ah! ah!
8va

SCINTILLE, DIAMANT

FROM LES CONTES D'HOFFMANN

BY JACQUES OFFENBACH

LIBRETTO BY JULES BARBIER AND MICHEL CARRÉ

First performance at Opéra-Comique, Paris, February 10, 1881

All through *The Tales of Hoffmann,* the poet-hero is dogged by an evil genius who takes four different incarnations (each a baritone). In the Venetian episode, this villain appears as a suave captain of infantry bent, like the devil he is, on capturing as many souls as he can. One instrument he employs for his fell purpose is an enormous diamond that he wears on a finger, and in this aria he calls upon the jewel to attract the courtesan Giulietta, through whose blandishments he has already destroyed the soul, represented by his reflection in a mirror, of one man and now hopes to secure the reflection of a second, that of Hoffmann. At the close of the aria he calls upon the diamond to summon Giulietta, who appears promptly and, before the act is much older, has succeeded in destroying Hoffmann's reflection. The name of the captain, who imperturbably glides in and out of the action to wreak his evil, is appropriately Dapertutto, which in Italian—*da per tutto*—means "everywhere."

Andante poco mosso
Andante poco mosso
pp
p
p
pp
espr.
Scin- til- le, di- a- mant,
Re- volve, dia- mond; re- flect,
Mi- roir où se prend l'a- lou- et-
Blue mir- ror mis- lead- ing the swal-
te, Scin- ti- le di- a- mant
low! Take ar- rows from the moon

fas— ci— ne, at— ti— re— la;
To dazzle, to kill, to di— rect!
L'a- lou— et— te ou la fem—
Be it swal— low, be it wom—
pp leggeriss
p
me A cet ap- pas vain-queur
an, They shall be ta— ken soon,
pp
Vont de l'aile ou du coeur;
Drawn to nest in your heart.

poco animato
L'une y lais se la vi
Cut the life from the swal
e Et l'autre y perd son â
low! From wo man shall her soul
me! L'une y lais- se la vi e Et l'autre y
part! Cut the life from the swal low! From wo-man
f allarg.
ff
Lento
f allarg.
col canto
perd son â me! Ah! Scin til
shall her soul part! Ah! Re volve,
a tempo
pp
fp a tempo
p
pp espr.
ppp

le, di — a — mant
dia-mond; re — flect,
Mi- roir où se prend l'a-lou- et-
Blue mir-ror mis-lead-ing the swal-
te Scin — til — le, di — a — mant, at — ti — re — la
low! Cold flame where he will die, Catch-ing the light,
rall.
at — ti — re — la,
Catch wo — man's eye!
rall.
p
espr.
at — ti — re la!
O draw her nigh!
Beau
Glow

di- a- mant, At- ti- re-
blue and white! I hold you
la! Beau di- a- mant,
high! Glow blue and white!
rall.
Scin- til- le! At- ti- re-
O dia- mond! O draw her
la!
nigh!
p
molto dim.
pp
ppp

LETTER SONG

FROM LA PERICHOLE

BY JACQUES OFFENBACH

LIBRETTO BY HENRI MEILHAC AND LUDOVIC HALÉVY

First performance at Théâtre des Variétés, Paris, October 6, 1868

In this operetta the traditional boy-loses-girl turn of plot comes not very long after the curtain has risen on Act I. La Perichole and Paquillo are a couple of street singers in nineteenth-century Peru who are very much in love with each other but who fail to earn a living because of Paquillo's jealousy. When Don Andres, the Viceroy, offers La Perichole a post as lady in waiting, she feels that she must accept just so that she can eat again. Asking Don Andres not for jewels, gold, a carriage, or a title, but merely a pencil, she composes a pathetic letter of farewell, full of grace and tenderness.

Ballet lovers will recognize the principal strain of the *Letter Song* as one of the finest melodies in the score of *Gaité Parisienne,* where it is introduced as the Baron and the Glove Seller dance a *pas de deux.*

Andante
p
O mon cher a-mant, je te ju-re, Que je
Be-lov-ed, I swear that no ri-val Has re-
mp
p
l'ai-me de tout mon coeur; mais-vrai, la-mi-sère est trop du-re, Et
placed you or ev-er will; Sim-ply, I like a chance of sur-viv-al, And
rit.
a tempo
nous a-vons trop de mal-heur
our chance has al-ways been ill.
Tu dois le com-pren-dre toi
You know I don't mean to re-
a tempo
rit.
p
mê-me, Que ce-la ne sau-rait du-rer
prove you, You know I am right in your heart.
Et
It's

47

rit.
qu'il vaut mieux, Dieu que je t'ai - me! Et qu'il vaut mieux nous sé - pa -
ter - ri - ble - God! how I love you; It's ter - ri - bly true we must
colla voce
rit.
a tempo
rer, Crois - tu qu'on puisse ê - tre bien ten - dre, A -
part. It is quite pic - tur-esque in the gut - ter, Though
lors que l'on man-que du pain? À quels trans-ports - peut on - s'at -
hard - ly i - deal for a bed; Com-fort and love pair like bread and
rit.
a tempo
Animez
ten - dre, En s'ai-mant quand on meurt de faim! Je suis fai-ble car je suis
but - ter, And the fact is we have no bread! Such a hun-ger must have an
rit.
a tempo

sf
fem - me, Et j'au - rais, ren - du quel - que jour, Le der - nier sou - pir, ma chère
end - ing: Am I weak? A wo - man am I. I might breathe my last Just in -
poco rit.
a tempo
â - me, Croy - ant en pous - ser un d'a - mour! Ces pa -
tend - ing An am - our - ous im - pul - sive sigh! Do you
collo voce
a tempo
ro - les là sont cru - el - les, Je le sais bien, mais que veux
fear I may act as I ought - n't? My words are hard, but fact is
tu? Pour les cho - ses es - sen - ti - el - les, Tu peux comp -
fact. And in what is real - ly im - por - tant, You can re -

rit.
a tempo
ter — sur ma - ver - tu. — Je t'a - do - re, si je — suis
ly on my vir - tue or tact. — If I seem to have lost — con-
rit.
a tempo
fol - le. C'est de toi — com - pte là des - sus! Et je
trol, Still do not think — me heart - less or crude. Yours for-
rit.
si - gne: la Pé - ri - cho - le, Qui t'ai - me, Mais qui — n'en peut
ev - er, La Pe - ri - chole, Who ad - ores you, but whose heart needs
rit.
a tempo
plus!
food.
mf
a tempo
rall.

VOCE DI DONNA

FROM LA GIOCONDA

BY AMILCARE PONCHIELLI

LIBRETTO BY TOBIA GORRIO (ARRIGO BOÏTO)

First performance at La Scala, Milan, April 8, 1876

The poor old lady who sings this aria is known simply as La Cieca, "the blind woman," and she is the mother of the heroine of the opera, a street singer known as La Gioconda, "the joyous girl." In the first act of the opera La Cieca is narrowly saved from the hands of an angry mob which thinks her a witch who has caused a popular gondolier to lose a sporting event. The mob is ordered back by the sudden appearance of Duke Alvise and his beautiful wife, Laura. When La Cieca hears Laura's kind words, she sings her this touching aria, offering the only gift she can—her rosary. Eventually the benediction that goes with the gift does work to Laura's advantage, for she departs from the scene, at the end of Act IV, in the arms—and the boat—of her lover. Not, however, before her jealous husband has almost succeeded in killing her with poison.

Andante sostenuto
La Cieca p dolciss. espress.
Vo-ce di don-na o d'an-ge-lo le mi-e ca-te-ne ha
Wom-an or an-gel, yours is the voice That, plea-ding, has lif-ted the
Andante sostenuto
p
sciol-to; mi vietan le mie te-ne-bre di
chains from me. You give my dark-ness cause to re-joice Though
allarg.
rall.
quel-la san-ta di quel-la san-ta il vol-to,
I, a-las can ne-ver see Your face my saint-ly sav-ior.
col canto
(hurrying)
pu-re da me non par-ta-si, da me non
Ah, but you must not leave me, though, With-out a
L.h.
L.h.

rall.
par - ta - si sen - za un pie - to - so don, no!
hum - ble gift, not that It can re - pay, no!
col canto
a tempo
no! A te que - sto ro - sa - rio
no! My ro - sa - ry I of - fer,
pp leggeriss.
a tempo
che le pre ghie - re a - du - na,
pray You ac - cept and keep it;
io te lo por - go ac - cet - ta - lo, ti por - te -
may It as - sure you hap - pi - ness And eve - ry

rà fortu na; sul-la tua tes-ta
gift of for tune. O may my be-ne-
p
vi-gi-li la mia be-ne-di-zion, sul-la tua
dic-tion well Pro-tect what I would bless! My be-ne-
pp
allarg. molto
a tempo
te sta, sul-la tua te sta vi-gi-li la
dic tion My be-ne-dic-tion pro-tect you well, Pro-
ff
allarg. molto e dim.
a tempo
mi-a be-ne di zion.
tect you whom I now bless!
pp
8va

CHE GELIDA MANINA

FROM LA BOHÈME

BY GIACOMO PUCCINI

LIBRETTO BY GIUSEPPE GIACOSA AND LUIGI ILLICA

First performance at Teatro Reggio, Turin, February 1, 1896

A pretty seamstress has knocked on the door of an artist's garret in Paris, to ask for help: her candle has gone out. Rodolfo, the artist, appreciates the situation—and the girl's good looks—and, when she drops her key, thoughtfully sees to it that his candle blows out as well. In semidarkness they search on the floor for the key; Rodolfo finds it and surreptitiously thrusts it into his pocket; and then, as the orchestra plays a single note, he grasps her little hand, comments on how cold it is, and gives her, unasked, a sketchy but very melodious summary of his life and philosophy of love and living. At its close he has the gallantry to ask her to return the compliment. He is already at least half in love.

Andante affetuoso
dolciss.
Che ge - li - da ma - ni - na, se la
How cold your lit - tle hand is! May I
pp
la - sci ri - scal - dar. Cer - car che gio — va? Al
keep it warm in mine? To search in dark — ness is
bu - io non si tro — va.
on - ly wast - ed la — bor.
l.h.
Ma per for - tu — na è una
But we are luck — y to -

rall.
not — te di lu — na, — e qui la lu — na l'ab-
night there is moon — light — And in this gar — ret the
affret.
poco rit.
a tempo
bia — mo vi — ci — na. A - spet - ti si - gno - ri - na, le di-
moon is our neigh - bor. If you'd re - main a lit - tle, In a
poco rit.
a tempo
rò con due pa — ro — le chi son, chi son,
mom - ent I could tell you My "who" and "why",
poco rall.
p
e che fac — cio, co — me — vi —
what my work is, what — I — live —
pp
a tempo
poco affrett.
a tempo

Andante sostenuto
vo. vuo — le? Chi son? chi
by. Will you? You will? In
son? sono un po - e - ta. Che co - sa fac - cio?
sum: I am a po - et; And so my work is
espress.
scri - vo. E co - me vi - vo? Vi - vo.
rhy - ming. What do I live by? Liv - ing!
dolce
rall.
Andante lento
In po - ver - tà mia lie - ta scia - lo da gran si -
Though poor I ne - ver show it When like a prince I

gno - re rime ed in - ni d'a - mo - re, Per so - gni e per chi -
squan - der All my coin - age of love - songs For i - ma - ges of
pp
me - re e per ca - stel - li in a - ria
won - der And for in - ven - tive fan - cies,
cresc.
allarg.
con moltiss. espress.
rit.
l'an - i - ma ho mi - lio - na - ria Ta -
No one is rich as I am! Yet
allarg.
f
rit.
lor dal mio for - zie - re ru - ban tutti i gio -
my fan - tas - tic trea - sur - y Glad - ly suf - fers the
con grande espress.
p
sostenuto

dolciss.
lel — li due la — dri: gli oc - chi bel — li V'en-
pi — ra — cy of wo — men's love — ly glan — ces. By
trar con voi pur o — ra ed i miei so - gni u-sa — ti
glan - cing should you flat — ter Dreams that are worn but gol — den,
dolciss.
con anima
e i bei so - gni mie - i — to - sto si di — le —
It is cer - tain those ri - ches — Quick - ly will dis — ap —
poco allarg.
p
molto rall.
a tempo
guar — mai l fur — to non m'ac - co — ra
pear — The theft will hard - ly mat — ter,
a tempo
dim.
molto rall.
pp

allarg.
poi-chè poi-chè v'ha pre-so stan - za la dol - ce spe -
Be-cause in their place I al - read - y Have hopes more en -
f con anima
cresc.
allarg.
ran - za!
dear - ing!
f dim.
p dolciss.
Or che mi co - no - sce - te
Now that you know of my life,
pp allarg. sempre
stentando
allarg.
par-la-te vo - i, deh! par-la-te. Chi sie - te
I beg a fa - vor: Don't be shy a - bout your life:
f con anima
allarg.
p
pp rall.
dim.
Vi piac-cia dir!
Will you re - ply?
col canto
ppp allarg. e dim. molto
Ped.

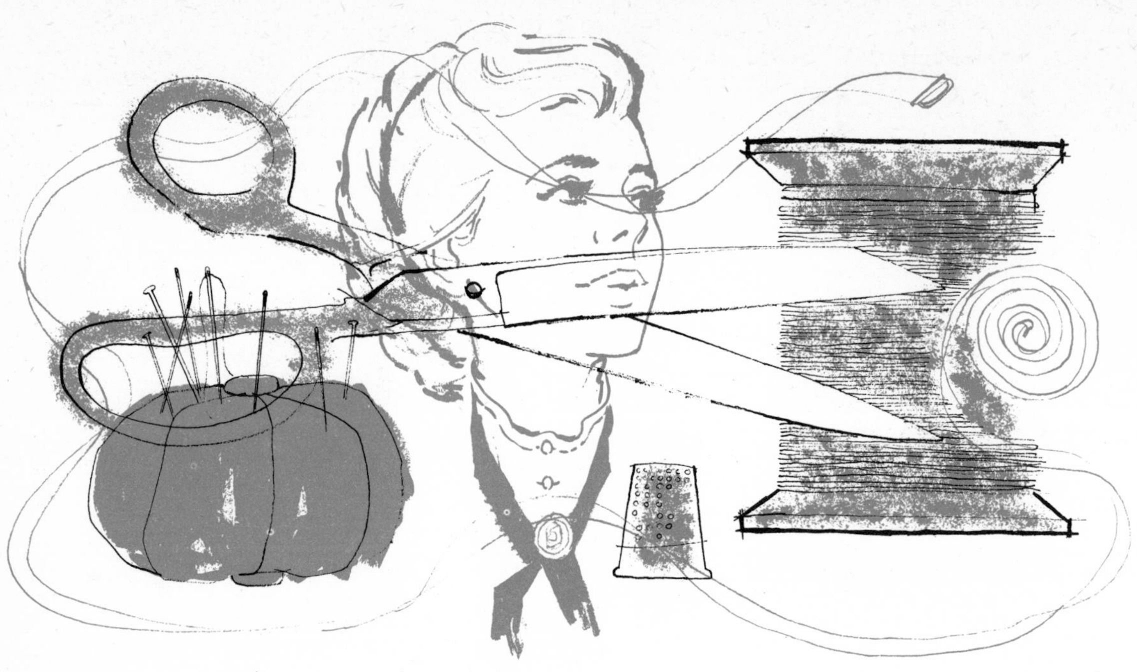

MI CHIAMANO MIMI

FROM LA BOHÈME

BY GIACOMO PUCCINI

LIBRETTO BY GIUSEPPE GIACOSA AND LUIGI ILLICA

First performance at Teatro Reggio, Turin, February 1, 1896

To Rodolfo's invitation to tell her story, Mimi responds simply and directly: "Yes. They call me Mimi, but my name is Lucy," and she artlessly—with some repetition and a naïve pleasure—speaks of her life and joy in such things as flowers and good spring weather. The musical contrast with Rodolfo's narrative reflects strikingly the differences in the personalities of the lovers—one warming up to a great flow of melody that reaches a climactic high note, the other beginning hesitantly with the little rising scale that always characterizes Mimi throughout the opera, then continuing mostly in short melodic phrases of narrow range, showing only glimpses of the emotional depths that lie beneath Mimi's sweet shyness.

It is Rodolfo's musical ardor that carries the day; for when they leave the garret a few minutes later to join his friends at the Café Momus, it is his melody that they sing in unison.

Andante lento
Si. Mi chia - ma - no Mi - mi, ma il mio
Yes, Mi - mi is what I'm called, But my
Andante lento
no - me è Lu - ci - a
name is Lu - ci - a.
La sto-ria mia è bre - ve
My sto - ry is a brief one
A tela o a
In silk and
se - ta ri - ca - mo in ca - sa e fuo - ri
can - vas I work em - broi - dered flow - ers,
Son tran - quil - la e
Keep - ing well con-
lie - ta ed è mio sva - go far gi - glie ro - se mi
tent - ed; To form a lil - y or rose de - lights me. I

Andante calmo (dolcemente)
piac — cion quel — le co — se che han si dolce ma -
like things half pa — the — tic With a gen - tle no -
Andante calmo
molto piano
lì — a, che par - la - no d'a - mor, di pri - ma -
stal — gia Sug - ges - ting love and spring, things that are
rit.
cresc.
col canto
pp
ve - re, che
scent - ed, Those
par - la - no di so - gni e di chi — me — re, quel - le
dreams and fan - cies where a joy is hint — ed, Mag - ic
pp

Rall.
a tempo
co — se che hanno - me po — e — si — a
sec — rets, all things we call po — et — ic.
Lei m'in-
Do you
rall.
a tempo
rall.
ten - de?
fol - low?
Lentamente
Mi chia-ma - no Mi - mì, il per -
Mi - mi is what I'm called; Why that
Lentamente
molto espress
chè non so.
is, who cares?
Allegretto mod.
So — la, mi fo il
All by my - self I
Allegretto mod.
p
poco rit.
pran-zo da me stes — sa. Non va - do sempre a mes-sa ma
take my meal at noon — day: I'm not at Mass each Sun-day, But
pp poco rit.

a piacere
pre - go as - sai il Sig - nor. Vi — vo so — la, so — let — ta
of - ten say my prayers. In my room I have no one;
col canto
a tempo
là in u - na bian — ca ca — me — ret — ta:
There as I sew my gaze is of - ten tak — en
a tempo
p
poco rall.
guar — do sui tet - ti e in cie — lo.
Ov — er the roof-tops to hea — ven.
pp poco rall.
Andante molto sostenuto
con molto anima
ma quan - do vien lo sge — lo il pri - mo so - le e
But when the buds a - wak — en, Kissed by the Ap - ril
Andante molto sostenuto
pp
cresc.
poco a poco

con grande espansione
mi — o — il pri — mo ba — cio del — l'a -
sun — shine, — There ev' — ry morn - ing come the
allarg.
pri — le e mi — o! — il pri — mo
ear — li — est sun — beams, — The sun is
allarg.
dim.
a tempo
rall.
so — le è mi — o! — Ger-
mine to a — wake in. — I
rall.
tempo andante (agitando appena)
sostenuto
mo — glia in un va — sou - na ro — sa fog lia a fog - lia la
place in my win — dow a rose — bud And I watch it un-
Tempo andante
pp
sostenuto

ten.
allarg.
spi — o! Co - sì gen - til il pro - fu — mo d'un
fold — ing: What grace the scent of a blos — som can
allarg.
col canto
calmo come prima
fior mai
be! But
calmo come prima
pp
poco rit.
p
fior ch'io fac — cio, ahi — mè! i fior ch'io
flow — ers made by me, Un - scen - ted
ppp
poco rit.
a tempo
fac — cio, ahi - mè, non han-no o - do — re!
ro — ses, are what my hands are hold — ing.
a tempo
pp
rall.

MUSETTA'S WALTZ

FROM LA BOHÈME

BY GIACOMO PUCCINI

LIBRETTO BY GIUSEPPE GIACOSA AND LUIGI ILLICA

First performance at Teatro Reggio, Turin, February 1, 1896

If the character of the first soprano in this opera, Mimi, is essentially sweet, shy, and retiring, that of the other soprano, Musetta, presents a brazen contrast—and so should the voices of the two members of the opera company in an ideal cast. Musetta's single aria occurs in the second act outside the Café Momus, where the grisette is sharing a sidewalk table with her current protector, the wealthy, elderly Alcindoro. At the next table are seated the Bohemians, including Musetta's old flame, Marcello. In Musetta's philosophy modesty is a commodity that never got a girl anywhere, and she shamelessly professes her own attractiveness to all and sundry, taking particular aim, however, at her quondam lover, Marcello, the artist. Her aim is precise: Marcello, bitter though he still is, takes up the tune; and before the short act is over, Alcindoro has been sent on a bootless errand while Musetta gets herself literally carried away by Marcello.

Tempo di Valzer lento
(con molta grazia eleganza)
Quan do me'n
When I go
Tempo di Valser lento
rall.
a tempo
vo' quan - do me'n vo' so - let - ta per la
out, when I go out a - lone to walk I
quasi rit.
via la gen - te sos - ta e mi - ra,
know The mas - cu - line re - ac - tions:
quasi rit.
e la bel - lez - za mi - a
Hal - ted by my at - trac - tions

appena allarg.
a tempo
tut - ta ri - cerca in me, ri - cerca in me da ca - po a
Each man will let his eye from top to toe Ap - prov - ing - ly
col canto
a tempo
ritendo
pie! ed as - sa -
go. O how I
p
ritendo
a tempo
molto rall.
po - ro al - lor la bra - mo - sia sot - til, che da gl'oc chi tra - spi - ra
sa - vor that in - ten - si - ty Of glance, looks that sharp - ly ad - mi - re,
a tempo
molto rall.
rit.
a tempo
e dai pa - le - si vezzi in - ten - der sa al - le oc -
That seem to pierce my flaunt - ed charms to see Oth - er
rit.
a tempo
f

poco rall.
a tempo
cul — te bel - tà.
beau — ties more coy.
Co - sì l'ef — flu — vio del de -
While in the tide of their de -
pp
a tempo
rit.
(short)
a tempo
si — o
si — re
tut - ta m'ag - gi - ra
That swells a - bout me,
fe - li - ce
I trem - ble
rit. molto
mf
a tempo
rall.
mi fa
with joy,
fe - li - ce
I trem - ble
mi fa!
with joy!
rall.
a tempo
E tu che sa — i
You, when with — out me
a tempo
pp

quasi rit.
quasi rit.
che me-mo-rie ti strug-gi, da me tan-to ri-
Are tor-tured by your me-mo-ry; Yet now you turn your
quasi rit.
fug-gi? So ben: le an-go-scie
back to me. You hope to keep your
tue non le vuoi dir. non le vuoi dir, so
hope-less love from view; But O my love, I
col canto
poco allarg.
a tempo
ben, ma ti sen-ti mo-rir!
know you will die if you do!
poco allarg.
a tempo

O MIO BABBINO CARO

FROM GIANNI SCHICCHI

BY GIACOMO PUCCINI

LIBRETTO BY GIOACHINO FORZANO

First performance at Metropolitan Opera House, New York, December 14, 1918

The cast of this one-act opera is inhabited largely by the vulturous relatives of a wealthy, just-dead Florentine, who attempt, even before the body is cold, to break his will. They can't think of a watertight way to do this, and a bright fellow named Gianni Schicchi is called in to help. Gianni, no saint himself, is so thoroughly disgusted with the crew that he is about to leave. His daughter, Lauretta, however, is in love with one of the relatives, and in this aria she begs him to change his mind. He does; but the relatives get little satisfaction in the end.

The tune is the sweetest and most easily remembered—if not the best—in the opera. Tinpan Alley may be expected to seize on it the moment it goes out of copyright. That, however, will not happen till 1974.

English version by Edoardo Petri

pp
a com-per - ar l'a - nel lo! Si, si, ci vog-lio an-
To buy our wed ding ring! Oh! yes, I real-ly
da re! e se l'a - mas si in - dar no, an-
love him, And if you still say No; I'll
drei sul Pon te Vec chio, ma per but - tar mi in
go to Pon te Vec chio, And throw my-self be -
Ar no! Mi strug - go e mi tor - men to! O
low. I lan - guish and I suf fer, A -

pp
Di - o, vor - rei mo -
las, I want to
pp
Ped.
rir!
die.
rinforzando
Bab - bo, pie - tà, pie - tà!
Dad - dy I pray, I pray.
bab - bo, pie - tà, pie -
Dad - dy I pray, I
m.d.
rit.
pp
Ped.
tà!
pray.
m.d.
rall.
m.s.
Ped.

UN BEL DÌ, VEDREMO

FROM MADAMA BUTTERFLY

BY GIACOMO PUCCINI

LIBRETTO BY LUIGI ILLICA AND GIUSEPPE GIACOSA

First performance at La Scala, Milan, February 17, 1904

It is three years since Lieutenant Benjamin Franklin Pinkerton, U.S.N., has left his fifteen-year-old bride, Butterfly, in Nagasaki. One fine morning her maid, Suzuki, tries to persuade her mistress (as she may have many times before) that Pinkerton is never going to come back. At first Butterfly is violently angry. Then she looks down the hill, from her house, to the harbor, and she sings this ecstatic aria, telling Suzuki exactly what it is that is going to happen.

It happens that same fine day, though not precisely as Butterfly described it. Pinkerton's ship, the *Abraham Lincoln,* steams into the harbor; he mounts the hill the next morning; and the presence of his American wife, Kate, tells the Japanese girl what she must do. She commits suicide.

The first performance of *Madama Butterfly* was a smashing failure. Yet even at that performance, which was marked by catcalls and curses from the audience, there was some applause for *Un bel di, vedremo.* And at the second performance, fourteen weeks later, *Un bel di, vedremo* had to be encored, and the composer himself stepped onto the stage to take a bow when the soprano was through. The whole evening, in fact, was a triumph.

Andante molto calmo ♩=42
Un bel di, ve-
One fine day we'll
mf
pp rall.
pp come da lontano
a tempo
dre-mo le-var-si un fil di fu-mo sul-l'e-
no-tice A thread of smoke a-ris-ing on the
poco rall.
stre-mo con-fin del ma-re. E poi la na-ve ap-pa-re
sea In the far ho-ri-zon, And then the ship ap-pear-ing

Un poco mosso
Poi la na - ve bian — ca en — tra nel — por — to,
Then the trim white ves — sel Glides — in - to the har — bour,
Un poco mosso
p
mf
Un poco mosso
con passione
ritenuto
rom - ba il suo sa — lu — to. Ve — di? E — ve -
Thun - ders forth her can — non. See you? now he is
f con passione
ritenuto
Un poco mosso
rall.
dolcemente
nu — to! Io non gli scen - do in - con — tro. Io no. Mi
com — ing! I do not go to meet him. Not I! I
dolcemente
rall.
pp
a tempo
con semplicita
met - to là sul ci — glio del col — le e a - spet - to,
stay up — on the brow of the hill — ock, And wait there,
pp
a tempo

e a — spet — to gran tem — po e non mi pe — sa, —
And wait for a long time, But nev - er wear - y —
rit.
a tempo
animando un poco
— la lun - ga at - te - sa.
— . of the long wait - ing.
Eu - sci - to dal - la
From out the crowd - ed
pp
rit.
a tempo
animando un poco
fol - la cit — ta — di — na — un uo - mo, un pic - ciol
cit - y there is com — ing — A man, a lit - tle
rall. un poco
pun — to s'av - via per la col — li — na. —
speck in the dis - tance, Climb - ing the hill — ock. —
rall. un poco

Sostenendo molto
Lo stesso movimento
Chi sa - rà? chi sa — rà? E co - me sa - rà
Can you guess who it is? And when he's reach'd the
giun - to che di - rà? che di - rà? Chia - me - ra But - ter -
sum - mit, Can you guess what he'll say? He will call, "But - ter -
rall.
dim.
Lento
fly dal - la lon - ta - na. Io sen - za dar ri - spo - sta me ne sta - rò na -
fly," from the dis - tance. I, with - out answ'ring, Hold my - self qui - et - ly con -
ppp
rall. molto
con molta passione
sco - sta un po' per ce - lia — e un po' per non mo -
ceal'd; A bit to tease him — And a bit so as not to
col canto

Andante come prima
con forza
ri — re al primo in - con - tro, ed e - gli alquanto in pe - na chia-me -
die — at our first meet - ing. And then, a lit - tle trou-bled, He will
Andante come prima
con molta passione
ff
p
rà, chia - me - rà Pic - ci - na mo - gliet - ti - na o - lez - zo di ver -
call, he will call, "Dear ba - by, wife of mine, Dear lit - tle orange
pp
be — na, i no - mi che mi da - va al suo ve — ni — re.
blos — som!" The names he used to call me when he came here.
3
3
Tut - to que - sto avver - rà te lo pro - met - to. Tien - ti la tua pa -
This will all come to pass as I tell you. Ban - ish your i - dle
f
f

u — ra, io con si - cu ra fe — de l'a —
fears — for he will re - turn, — I
Largamente
ff
spet — to.
know — it.
Largamente
fff
meno
f
dim.
rit.
p a tempo
pp sostenuto
mf
p

RECONDITA ARMONIA

FROM TOSCA

BY GIACOMO PUCCINI

LIBRETTO BY LUIGI ILLICA AND GIUSEPPE GIACOSA

First performance at Teatro Constanzi, Rome, January 14, 1900

Mario Cavaradossi, the hero of the opera, is a painter, and in Act I he goes to work on a canvas depicting the Magdalen. It is partly done, and he gazes in admiration at the beauty he has created, an amalgamation of his beloved Tosca's dark beauty, and the blond attractions of an unknown lady whom he sketched the day before as she was praying in church. As he sings, he takes out a medallion of *"la bruna Tosca,"* and he realizes that no matter what use he may make of the blond one's coloring, Tosca is the only one he thinks about. The mysterious lady happens to be the Countess Attavanti, and when the jealous Tosca recognizes her a little later in the act, Cavaradossi has a bit of explaining to do. Fortunately for the props department of opera companies, the Attavanti never appears on the stage, and the local dauber is not called upon to create the *recondita armonia* (recondite harmony) of the multifarious beauties.

Andante lento
Original in F
Più lento
Re —— con-di ta ar - mo - ni - a
Har —— mon-ious - ly in con - trast,
Più lento
dolciss.
r.h.
l.h.
sostenuto
di bel - lez - za di - ver - se!
Two un - match - a - ble beau - ties:
È bru - na, Flo - ri - a, l'ar -
How dark is Tos - ca's hair, My
sostenuto
rall
a tempo
den - te a - man - te mi - a
pas - sion - ate be - lov - ed,
e te, bel - tà dei -
While yours, un - known one,
rall.
a tempo

gno ta cin-ta di chio-me
gol-den-ly fair, Seem the au-ra of
bion-de! Tu az-zur-ro hai
calm in its pride! You have eyes of
l'oc-chio To-sca ha l'oc-chio
sky blue; and my love is
ne-ro
black-eyed.
lo stesso tempo
p
L'ar-te nel suo mi-
Art by ar-cane se-
3
p

rall.
ste — ro le di - ver - se bel - lez - ze in - siem con - fon - de; ma
lec — tion Takes the dark of the known to light the un - known. Yet
col canto
I° Tempo
nel ri - trar co — ste — i il mio so - lo pen -
ev — en as I im — age Her in - car - nate per -
I° Tempo
sie - ro, ah! il mio sol pen - sier sei tu!
fec - tion, Know my thoughts in hom — age Yours,
f
allarg. rit.
To — sca, sei tu!
To — sca, a — lone!
allarg.
col canto
p
188

VISSI D'ARTE

FROM TOSCA

BY GIACOMO PUCCINI

LIBRETTO BY LUIGI ILLICA AND GIUSEPPE GIACOSA

First performance at Teatro Constanzi, Rome, January 14, 1900

In the second act of *Tosca* the suave Roman chief of police, Scarpia, has made the conventional offer of the villain of melodrama to its heroine: her beautiful body in return for the life of her lover. Cavaradossi, he says, shall be hanged within the hour unless she consents. It is at this point that the distracted prima donna sings her passionate aria, ending with a plea to God, whom she has always served with song. God does not intervene: Tosca helps herself by murdering her tormentor.

Puccini did not want to write an extended aria at this point: he claimed it held up the action. Nevertheless, he did it so well that it is the high point of the opera for the soprano who sings it, and often for the audience too. The story goes that at a rehearsal in Vienna, Maria Jeritza, who was singing the role, slipped off the couch just as her cue for this aria came from the orchestra. She sang the whole piece lying prone on the floor, whereupon the composer, who was supervising the production, cried: "That's good; it gives the aria some life!" Jeritza thereafter always sang the aria horizontal.

Andante lento appassionate
p dolciss. con grande sentimento
Original in Eb minor
Vis - si d'ar - te, vis - si d'a - mo - re, non fe - ci mai
Love I lived by, mu - sic I lived for; No per - son or
pp con molta dolcezza
ma - le ad a - ni - ma vi - va! Con man fur — ti — va
crea - ture have I af — flict - ed! Free - ly in qui — et
Poco allarg. con anima
quan - te mi - se - rie co - nob - bi aiu - ta - i
Have not my cha - ri - ties ev - er been gi - ven?
f Poco allarg. con anima
pp poco rall.
con grande sentimento
Sem - pre — con fe sin — ce — ra la mia pre -
Al - ways — in faith of hea - ven, At saint - ed

ghie — ra ai san - ti ta - ber - na - co - li sa - li. Sem - pre con
al — tars, My prayer with sim - ple pi — e — ty a - rose. In faith of
con anima
fè sin - ce — ra die — di fio - ri a - gl'al - tar. Nel -
hea - ven al — ways Lay my so - lace and re - pose. And
pp
cresc.
f dim.
p
l'o - ra del do — lo — re per — chè, per - chè, Si - gno - re, per -
now when love is plead — ing It's woe - ful des - pe — ra — tion, O
pp
chè me ne ri - mu - ne - ri co - sì?
God, can you for - get me in my need?
dolciss.
Die - di gio -
Do not my
pp
ppp

iel — li del - la Ma - don - na al man — to e die — di il
gems a — dorn the Ma - don - na's man — tle? Has not my
can - to a-gli a-stri al ciel, che ne ri-dian più bel-li — Nel - l'o-ra del do - lor per -
mu - sic been lift-ed high In ho-ly de - di — ca-tion? Will hea-ven take no heed of
cresc. molto
chè, per - chè — Si - gnor, ah! —
pain? O why, dear God, Why, God, —
cresc. molto
molto allarg.
rall.
per-chè me ne ri — mu — ne — ri co — si?
O why have you a — ban — doned me in need?
a tempo
sostenuto
col canto
pp
ppp

CHANT HINDOU

FROM SADKO

BY NIKOLAI RIMSKY-KORSAKOFF

LIBRETTO BY THE COMPOSER AND VLADIMIR IVANOVICH BYELSKY

First performance at Private Opera House, Moscow, January 7, 1898

Midway in the opera the hero Sadko has won a merchant fleet for his fellow Novgorodians and determines to choose where to trade with it by setting up a kind of song contest. Three merchants who happen to be present, a Viking, a Hindu, and a Venetian, sing a song apiece in praise of their native lands. It is the Venetian, a baritone, who wins with a barcarole that is seldom sung except in performances of the complete opera. The Viking's song has found a place in the repertoire of many a Russian concert basso. The *Song of India,* however, has been transcribed from its original tenor register for practically every voice or solo instrument ever invented, so great is its popularity.

The melody is built largely on a succession of major and minor thirds, and it achieves its languorous, exotic effect by a series of chromatic descents from the top to the bottom of these short intervals.

Original in G
p
p dolce
Les di - a - mants chez nous sont in - nom - bra - bles; Les per - les
With count - less dia - monds are the tem - ples gleam - ing, Our seas are
dans nos mers in - cal - cu - la - bles; C'est l'In - de ter - re des tré - sors.
rich with pearls beyond all dreaming: Our treasured In - dia, fa - ble's home!
(pp)
Hors des flots ti - è
From its glow ing wa

des
Un
ru
bis
s'é
lè
ters,
ah!
one
ru
by
ri
ve.
Le
phé
nix
S'y
po
ses!
Lo!
the
death
less
phoe
se,
Jeu
ne
fille
aux
trais
nix
soars
a
bove
the
bright
purs.
Jour
et
nuit
il
chan
te,
foam,
Ri
ses
ev
er
sing
ing,

più p
Sa - chan-son su - a — ve, —
Sing - ing_ of_ Nir - va — na, —
più p
mf
Et — ses - gran — des ai —
in — a _ tire — less wing —
mf
les — sur — la — mer — s'é - ten —
ing — Where — the_ pure — air_ glis —
mp
dent. — On — perd à — l'en - ten —
tens! — Of — the_ world — for - get —
p
p

pp
dre sou ve - nir du mon
ful is the world that lis
pp
p
espr.
de. Les di - a - mants chez nous sont in - nom - bra - bles, Les per - les
tens! With count-less dia - monds are the tem - ples gleam-ing, Our seas are
poco rit.
dans nos mers in - cal - cu - la - bles, C'est l'In - de ter - re
rich with pearls be-yond all dream - ing: Our treas-ured In - dia,
poco rit.
pp
des trés - sors.
fab - le's home!
pp

LA CALUNNIA

FROM IL BARBIERE DI SIVIGLIA

BY GIOACHINO ANTONIO ROSSINI

LIBRETTO BY CESARE STERBINI

First performance at Teatro Argentina, Rome, February 5, 1816

The Barber deals with the theme of dozens of other eighteenth- and early nineteenth-century comedies—an elderly man who aspires to marry a young girl, usually his ward. *The Barber's* old man is Dr. Bartolo; his ward, Rosina. In the second scene the doctor hears from Rosina's music teacher, Basilio, that the wealthy Count Almaviva has been seen in the neighborhood and that it may be the Count who is Rosina's unidentified suitor. How to get rid of him? Just start—quite gracefully, of course—some nasty rumor about him. Gossip will do the rest, says Basilio; and then he proceeds to describe graphically just how, like a gentle breeze, a small calumny may grow to the proportions of a storm, blasting a man as though it were a cannon.

The aria is wonderfully apt and effective, especially when sung on the stage. Basilio, being of one of the learned professions, wears a long black cloak and shovel hat, lending an air of comic evil to the proceedings. Usually the role is assigned to a basso of considerable stature; and as the orchestra builds its great crescendos, going up and down the scale in chattering single steps, the singer may rise from a sitting posture to unfold his full length, spread out his arms, and give other signals of the overwhelming power of slander. One would think that the clever verses of Sterbini had inspired a specially appropriate piece of music for the occasion. The odd fact, however, is that Rossini borrowed this music from *Sigismondo,* a serious opera he had produced only fourteen months before *The Barber,* and a resounding failure.

Allegro
p sotto voce
La ca - lun-nia è un ven - ti-cel - lo,
Like a zeph-yr be - gins a ca - lum - ny
un' au - ret-ta as - sai gen - ti - le,
O so gen-tly you bare - ly hear it,
che in-sen - si - bi - le, sot - ti - le, leg-ger-men - te, dol - ce - men - te
In - sub-stan-tial as a spir - it, None re-mark it, who could fear it?

in - co - min - cia, in - co - min - cia a su - sur - rar.
Less a whis - per than an in - ex - pres - sive sigh.
p
pp
Pia - no pia - no, ter - ra
Pia - no pia - no, hard - ly
ter - ra, sot - to vo - ce,
hin - ted, Sot - to vo - ce,
si - bil - lan - do va scor - ren - do, va scor -
al - most coo - ing, Half re - luc - tant it starts

ren — do, va, ron-zan-do, va ron-zan —
brew — ing Where it gains an ear's ad-mis —
simile
cresc. poco a poco
do; nel-l'o-rec-chie del-la gen-te s'in-tro-
sion, Then more loud in its trans-mis-sion In tran
du-ce s'in-tro-du-ce de-stra-men-te, e le tes-te ed i cer-
si-tion Lin-gers in the brain a min-ute, In the brain re-mains and
vel-li, e le tes-te ed i cer-vel-li fa stor-di-re, fa stor-
in it To more deaf-en-ing pro-por-tions, To more deaf-en-ing pro-

di - re, fa stor - di - re e far gon - fiar
por - tions Is al - lowed to am - pli - fy!
f
Dal - la boc - ca fuo - ri u-scen-do
From the lips the in - nu - en - do
p
lo schia maz-zo va cre-scen-do,
Starts an-oth-er mad cre-scen-do,
pren-de for-za a po-co a
Slow-ly gath-er-ing its
cresc.
po - co
for-ces
vo-la già di lo - co in lo - co, sembra il tuo-no, la tem-
Far and wide the ru-mor cour-ses Till at last it shall re-
f

pe - sta che nel sen del - la fo - res - ta va fischian - do, bron - to-
sem - b le storms that make the fo - rest trem - ble When the light - ning and the
8va
lan - do, e ti fa d'or - ror ge - lar, Al - la fin tra boc - ca e
thun - der Lash in hor - ror from on high! Soon from ev' - ry mouth re-
ff
scop - pia si pro - pa - ga si rad - dop - pia e pro - du - ce un e - splo-
doub - led, By no op - po - si - tion troub - led, On it roars to its con-
sio - ne co - me un col - po di can - no
clus - ion In a fu - ri - ous ex - plo
f
ff

ne, co-me un col-po di can - no ne, un tre-muo-to un tem-po-
sion, In a fu - ri - ous ex - plo sion, A bom-bard-ment, an er-
ff
ra - le, un tre-muo-to un tem-po - ra - le, un tre-muo-to un tem-po-
up - tion, A bom-bard-ment, an er - up - tion, A bom-bard-ment, an er-
ra - le che fa l'a - ria rim-bom - bar, un tre-muo - to un tem - po -
up - tion Flings the ci - ty to the sky! A bom-bard-ment, an er-
ra - le, un tre - muo - to un tem - po - ra - le, un tre-muo-to un tem - po -
up - tion, A bom-bard-ment, an er - up - tion, A bom-bard-ment, an er-

ra - le che fa l'a-ria rim-bom-bar! E il me-
up-tion Flings the ci-ty to the sky! And the
p
schi - no ca - lun - nia - to, av - vi - li - to, cal-pe - sta - to, sot-to il
sub - ject, the sen - sa - tion Of this deft cal - um-ni - a - tion Hav - ing
colla parte
cresc.
pub - bli - co fla - gel - lo per gran sor - te va a cre -
lost his re - pu - ta - tion Has no choice now but to
p
cresc.
p
par. E il me - schi - no ca - lun - nia - to, av - vi - li - to, cal - pe
die! And the sub - ject, the sen - sa - tion of this deft cal - um - ni-
f
p

1.
sta-to, sot-to il pub-bli-co fla-gel-lo per gran sor-te va a cre-par.
a-tion Hav-ing lost his re-pu-ta-tion Has no choice now but to die!
p
2.
par, Sot-to il pub-bli-co fla-gel-lo per gran sor-te va a cre-
die! Hav-ing lost his re-pu-ta-tion Has no choice now but to
f
par, sot-to il pub-bli-co fla-gel-lo per gran sor-te va a cre-
die, Hav-ing lost his re-pu-ta-tion Has no choice now but to
par, sì, va a cre-par, sì, va a cre-par, sì, va a cre-par!
die! He has to die, He has to die, He has to die!
ff

AMOUR, VIENS AIDER MA FAIBLESSE!

FROM SAMSON ET DALILA

BY CAMILLE SAINT-SAËNS

LIBRETTO BY FERDINAND LEMAIRE

First performance at Grand Ducal Theater, Weimar, December 2, 1877

And it came to pass afterward that he loved a woman in the valley of Sorek, whose name was Delilah. Judges 16:1.

And it was Delilah, as everyone knows, whom the lords of the Philistines chose to find the secret of Samson's strength, the strength that had set his people free. In the opera she awaits her lover in her home, and she is decked with all the seductive charm she knows so well how to use. But she is not content to rely merely on her own beauty. In this powerful second act aria she calls upon the god of love to aid her in conquering the hitherto invincible warrior, and she ends on an ominously soft phrase close to the bottom of the contralto register.

Moderato
mf
A - mour!
O love,
f
dim.
pp
viens ai - der ma fai - bles — se! Ver - se le poi-
lend your strength to my weak — ness; Con - quer him that
son dans son sein!
I have but charmed.
Fais que, vain -
Poi - son his
sf
p
cu par mon a - dres — se, Sam -
heart with hea - ted vi — sions, By
pp

son soit en-chaî - né de - main!
mor - ning let him lie dis-armed!
cresc.
dim.
p
Il voud-rait en vain de son â - me Pou-voir me chas-ser, me ban-
Cau-tion bids him vain-ly to shun me; He can-not re-fuse what he
3
p
cresc.
rir! Pour-rait il é - tein - dre la flam - me Qu'a - li-
fears. What I am he knows, and the im - age Burns the
p
dim
p
men - te le sou - ve - nir? Il est à
more as it more en - dears. Sam - son shall
dim.
pp

moi! c'est mon es-cla ve! Mes
fall! With love be con quered! Be-
frè res crai - gnent son cour-roux;
fore his strength my bro-thers flee.
accel.
accel.
moi, seule en-tre tous, je le
I, I here al - one, dare de-
cresc.
bra
fy
a tempo
a tempo
f
p

ve Et le re – tiens à mes ge -
him; He shall be made a slave by
noux! A -
me! O
cresc.
f
f
mour! viens ai - der ma fai - bles
love, lend your strength to my weak
p
se! Ver se le poi - son dans son
ness; Con quer him that I have but

sein! Fais que, vain-
charmed. Poi - son his
f
p
cu par mon a - dres - se, Sam-
heart with hea - ted vi - sions By
son soit en - chaî - né de main!
morn - ing let him lie dis - armed!
dolce
pp
Con - tre l'a - mour sa force est
Love takes his strength to feed his
pp

vai — ne; Et lui, le
weak — ness, And he, the
fort par - mi les forts, Lui, qui d'un
stron - gest fights in vain. He who a -
peu — ple rompt la chaî — ne,
lone un — chained his peo — ple,
Suc - com - be - ra sous mes ef - forts!
I know I shall a - lone en - chain!
pp
dim.
8va

MON COEUR S'OUVRE À TA VOIX

FROM SAMSON ET DALILA

BY CAMILLE SAINT-SAËNS

LIBRETTO BY FERDINAND LEMAIRE

First performance at Grand Ducal Theater, Weimar, December 2, 1877

It is night when Samson finally approaches Delilah's house, determined to say only farewell and to end the affair. But Delilah's seductiveness is too much for his patriotic scruples. It grows late, and a storm begins to break. It is at this point in the second act that Delilah sings to him the most familiar melody in the opera, and perhaps the best known in the whole repertoire of contralto arias. The staccato accompanying figure in the first half of the aria may be taken to suggest the falling of the rain. When the music is performed on the operatic stage, it is Samson who sings the final phrase. In a second stanza the accompaniment adds a wind effect to the rain; and with the reappearance of the second half of the melody (in 4/4 time), Samson adds a tenor obbligato.

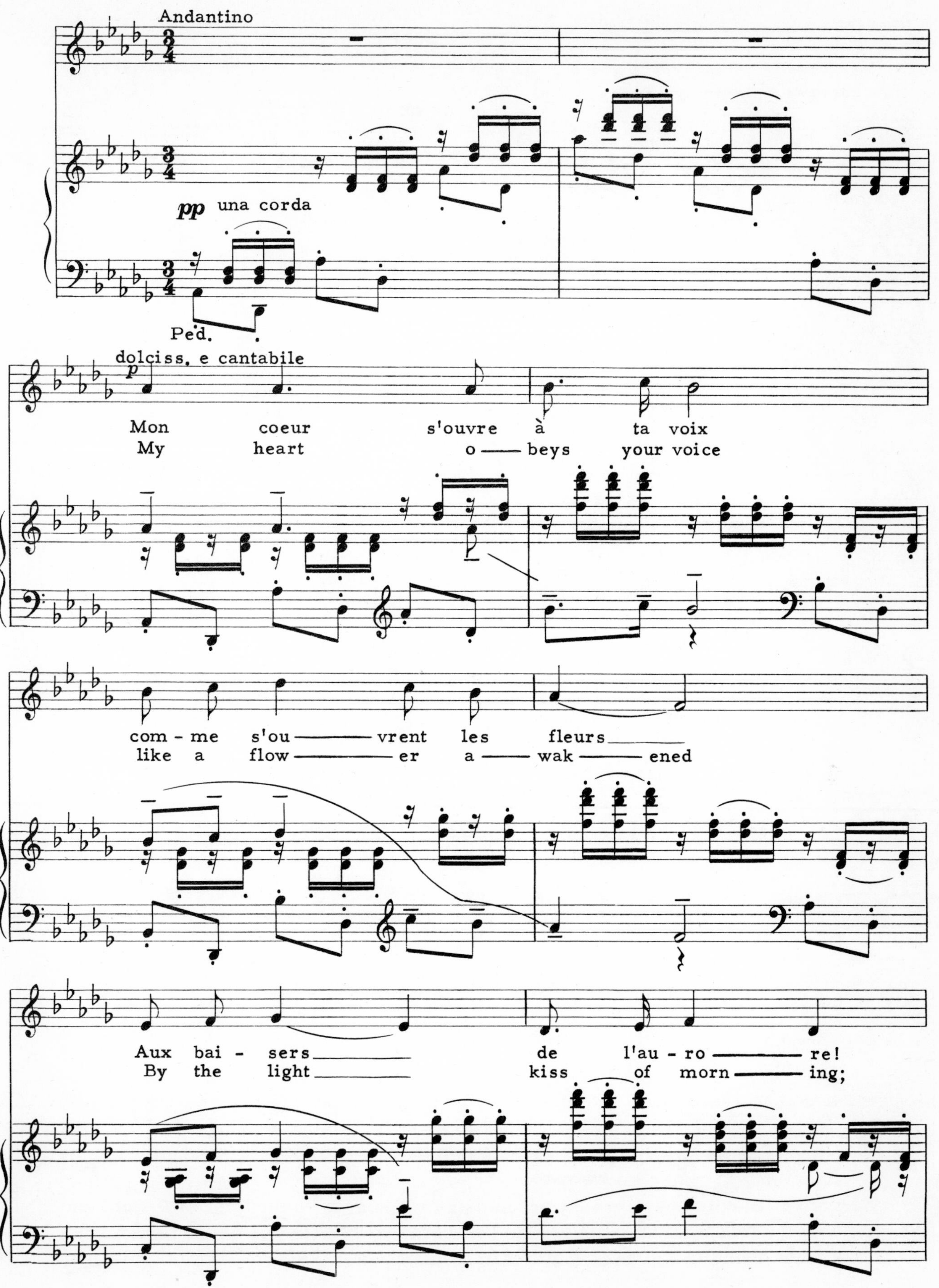
Andantino
pp una corda
Ped.
dolciss. e cantabile
p
Mon coeur s'ouvre à ta voix
My heart o — beys your voice
com - me s'ou — vrent les fleurs
like a flow — er a — wak — ened
Aux bai - sers de l'au - ro — re!
By the light kiss of morn — ing;
5

espress.
simile
Mais, ô mon bien-ai-mé,
O my be-lov-ed, speak!
pour mieux sé-cher mes pleurs,
Your si-lence is like dark-ness
dim.
Que ta voix parle en-co-re!
And I weep its re-turn-ing!

rinf.
Dis-
O
moi qu'à Da — li — la tu re-
say De — li — lah still holds your
rinf.
viens pour ja — mais! Re -
heart in her sway! Say
dis à ma ten — dres — se Les ser -
you've no will to leave me! Once a -

Stringendo
ments d'au - tre — fois,
gain let me hear
Stringendo
cresc.
l.h.
cresc.
ces ser - ments que j'ai — mais!
love com - mands all you say!
l.h.
mf
mf
ritard e dim.
Un peu plus lent
dolce
Ah! ré -
Speak your
8va
cantabile
Ped.
*
ponds à ma ten -
tri umph in sur -
Ped.
*
Ped.
*

dres — se Ver — se —
ren — der! Be — the —
Ped. *
moi — ver - se - moi — l'i -
god — Your con - sent — will —
cresc. sans presser.
vres — se! Ré — ponds — à ma ten -
prove you! Be strong — in be - ing
cresc.
più f
dres — se Ré — ponds — à ma ten-
ten — der! Be strong — in be - ing

f
dres - se! Ah! ver - se
ten - der! Ah! Be the
f
moi ver - se moi l'i
god Your con - sent will
dim.
p
vres - se! Sam-son! Sam-son!
prove you! Hear me, Sam-son,
molto espress.
pp
p
je t'ai - me!
I love you!
dim.

LETTER SCENE

FROM EUGEN ONEGIN

BY PETER ILYITCH TCHAIKOVSKY

LIBRETTO BY THE COMPOSER

First performance in Moscow, March 29, 1879

Into the life of a beautiful young Russian girl, Tatiana, strolls a world-weary man about town named Eugen Onegin. He is paying a casual call on the family in the company of his good friend, the poet Vladimir Lenski, who is engaged to marry Tatiana's sister. Onegin does not do much more than stroll with Tatiana by a lake and tell her a bit of his family's history, but the girl falls feverishly and romantically in love with him. That night she finds it impossible to sleep, and toward morning she writes Onegin a long, frank letter—foolish, indiscreet, but utterly sincere. We have here only the closing pages of this long scene, which is built up with great sweetness, subtlety, and deep feeling.

Tchaikovsky composed this scene before he did anything else with the opera. He himself had received a love letter from a girl he hardly knew; and though he did not find her attractive, he did what he considered the honorable thing and married her. It turned out to be a disastrous mistake. Onegin behaved, in his own opinion, just as honorably but more sensibly: he told Tatiana in the kindest way he could that he could love her only as a brother. His decision, however, turned out to be just as bad as Tchaikovsky's. Some years later he fell in love with Tatiana, but by this time she was married to another.

Andante
with feeling
Original in Db Major
Sag bist als Schutzgeist du ge - sen - det,
"Are you an an - gel sent to guide me
molto espress.
hast als Ver - su - cher mich ge - blen - det?
Or but a temp - ter who'd mis - lead me?
Gieb Antwort, los die Zwei - fel mir! —
Re - solve my doubts of what you seem. —
Hat mich das Traum - ge - sicht be - tro - gen,
Is quite an - oth - er out - come fa - ted?

222

fand ich ein Trug-bild nur in dir,
Is this a self-de-cep-tive dream
ist je-de Se-lig-keit ge-lo-gen?
By my un-world-li-ness cre-a-ted?
p
Molto più mosso
p
Sei's wie es will, mein ganz Ge-schick ist an das Traumge-
It must be more! Though I be wrong To beg for love so
p
leggero
sicht ge-bun - den! Du bist mein Sehn - nen,
in-dis-creet - ly, My fate, my soul, to

bist mein Gluck, durch dich al - lein, durch dich al - lein werd' ich ge -
you be - long, to you be - long And must con - fide them - selves com -
rit.
Tempo I
f appass.
sun - den! Be - den - ke nur, ich bin al - lein!
plete - ly! On no - one else can I re - ly:
rit.
f
Gar nie - mand will mich hier ver - ste - hen!
Who else would un - der - stand my pain here?
Più mosso
f
Und hülf - los muss ich un - ter - ge - hen wenn du nicht
Could I my tremb - ling hopes ex - plain here? And were I
p
cresc.

willst mein Ret - ter sein: Ich bau' auf dich, ich bau' auf
si - lent, I should die! I wait my life, I wait my
ff
accel.
dich, du musst mich hö - ren; ein ein - zig
life in your de - ci - sion: One word of
f
mf
Wort des Tro - stes sprich, doch straft ver - dien - ter Vor - wurf mich, so wird ein
ten - der - ness from you Will prove my vi - sion had been true Or, by re -
ff
rall.
ein - zig Wort so wird ein Wort den Traum zer - stö -
proach - ing me, Your just re - proach will break that vi -
colla voce
mf
rall.

Tempo I
ren!
sion!
ff
marcato
f
ff
f
Piu mosso
ff

Ich schlies - se!
I've signed it.
Oh! ver - stoss mich nicht! Miss-brau-che nim-mer mein Ver-trau-en!
Weak with shame I end. I can't re-read it. Dare I move him?
f dim.
p
f
Auf dich, du hol-des Traum-ge-sicht, auf dei - ne
But on his hon-or I de-pend As brave - ly,
p cresc.
f
Più vivo
ff
Eh re will ich bau en!
deep ly as I love him!
6
6
6
ff

LENSKI'S ARIA

FROM EUGEN ONEGIN

BY PETER ILYITCH TCHAIKOVSKY

LIBRETTO BY THE COMPOSER

First performance in Moscow, March 29, 1879

At a formal dance in the country, the worldly-wise Onegin amuses himself by paying particular attention to Olga, the pretty fiancée of his friend Lenski. Lenski becomes more and more annoyed, and when Onegin taunts him by comparing his bitter looks to those of Childe Harold, Byron's romantic hero, a challenge to duel ensues.

Neither of the friends really wants to duel, but both consider themselves too deeply committed to be able to back out with honor. The meeting is set for early the next morning beside a mill by a stream, and it is Lenski, the poet, who arrives first. While he waits, he sings this aria, which has come to be known as *Lenski's Air,* the best known (after the *Song of India*) tenor aria in Russian opera. The opening descending scale is characteristic of much of the pathetic love music throughout the work.

The premonition of death which Lenski sings of is only too well justified. He falls with Onegin's first shot.

Andante, assai adagio
Wo-hin, wo-hin, wo-hin seid ihr ent-schwunden, o
Where-to, where-to, where-to have you been ta-ken My
Ju-gend-zeit, o Lie-bes-glück?
youth-ful years, my joy in love?
stringendo
cresc.
espr.
a piena voce
Was wird der näch-ste Tag mir
What in the fut-ure waits me
a tempo
rit.
brin-gen? Mein Blick ver-mag nicht zu durch-drin-gen was
hid-den? To see that realm re-mains for-bid-den: Its

mir ver-birgt der Zu-kunft Schoos
dark-some na-ture is to wait.
Was frag'ich? Je-den trifft sein
So be it. All en-dure their
Loos:
fate.
'sist gleich, ob ich des To-des Beu-te ob
If Death soon pierce me with his ar-row Or
sf
p
mich ver-schont des Geg-ners Blei, von Gott kommt Al-les, wie's auch
if the ar-row pass me by, As God wills must we live or
poco rit.
sei, Er lenkt das Gestern und das Heu— te, Er sen-det
die: To yes-ter-day He pins to— mor— row, He bless-ed
mf
colla parte

p
uns des Ta-ges Pracht, Er sen-det uns die dun — kle Nacht.
gives the day its light, He blessed gives the dark — of night.
poco stringendo
p
Più mosso
Der-weil der Tag zu neu-em Le-ben im Glanz des Frühroth's auf-er-
The sun will climb the vault of hea-ven, Re-veal-ing much my song would
mf
wacht wird mich vielleicht, ach! schon um-ge-ben ge-heim-niss-vol-
crave, While I to si-lence may be giv-en With-in the mys-
cresc.
cresc.
- le Gra-bes-nacht, wo der Ver-ges-sen-heit zum Rau-be mein
- t'ry of the grave; And one young po-et, there un-fol-lowed, In
f
f

f
rit.
dim.
Na — me wird sammt meinem Stau - be! Wie bald ver-gisst die Welt! doch du!
tor — pid Le-the will be swal - lowed. The world will soon forget; but you,
mp
p
doch du —
you, Ol-ga,
ge-denkst noch
Will you for-
dim.
Tempo I
mein, — wenn ich im Gra-be ruh', — ja kom-men wirst Du wei-nend
get — me here as quick-ly too? — Or will you to my grave re-
pp
kla-gen und den-ken: Mir war einst ge-weiht — die Lie-be
tur-ning In tears think: I pos-sessed his love; — I had the

f
sei - ner Ju - gend - zeit ein Strahl des Glücks nach dunk - len Ta - gen! Ach,
de - di - ca - tion of His stor - my day's un - hap - py morn - ing. O
ff
Ol - ga, dich hab' ich ge - liebt! O wel che Se - lig - keit doch
Ol - ga, you pos - sessed my love! And you on - ly lit with in - spi
p
poco più animato
giebt ein Strahl des Glücks nach
ra - tion. My stor - my day's un -
p
dunklen Ta gen! Ach Ol ga, ich hab' dich ge -
hap - py morn ing. O Ol ga, you a - lone I
rit.
p

Stringendo
cresc. poco a poco
liebt!
love!
O komm zu mir, mein Lieb-chen traut, o
Be — lo — ved heart, my bride to be, my
string.
p
cresc.
Andante mosso
ff
komm zu mir! dein Bräut' gam ruft, er
bride-to - be, The dawn is near, draw
mf
harrt der hol-den Braut, er harrt der hol-den Braut! O
near, O love, to me! Draw near, O love, to me! Draw
rit.
ad lib.
p
komm o, komm_ ich har - re dein, mein Liebchen traut o komm zu
near, Draw near!_ Dear-ly be-lov'd, my bride-to - be, The dawn is
rit.
colla voce
p

234

a tempo
cresc.
mir, du hol — de Braut! Wo-hin, wo-
near, draw near — to me! Where-to Where-
pp
8va
hin, wo-hin seid ihr ent-schwun-den, o Ju — gend-
to, where-to have you been tak - en My youth — ful
cresc.
rit.
zeit, un-fass-bar sel'-ges Lie — bes-
years, my brief and ho-ly joy — in
mf
rit.
p
a tempo
glück!
love?
a tempo
pp
35

CONNAIS-TU LE PAYS?

FROM MIGNON

BY CHARLES LOUIS AMBROISE THOMAS

LIBRETTO BY MICHEL CARRÉ AND JULES BARBIER

First performance at Opéra-Comique, Paris, November 17, 1866

In the courtyard of a tavern, where there are many customers, appears a band of gypsies led by a ruffian named Jarno. In the band is a little creature, shy, sensitive, and so dressed in rags that one cannot be sure of her sex. This is Mignon; and when Jarno brutally demands that she perform an egg dance for the company, she works up the courage to refuse. Jarno begins to beat her but is finally dissuaded, partly by force, partly by money, and most of all by a pistol in the hands of Wilhelm, the hero of the opera, who thoughtfully makes his first entrance at that moment.

A little later in the first act Wilhelm tries to find out who the strange little creature really is. In answer to his questions, she sings this aria, the loveliest melody in the opera, which is also used effectively in the familiar Overture. Mignon is a vague and deeply disturbed little girl, and her answer to Wilhelm is necessarily unspecific. For she does not recall that the land "where the orange trees grow" is Italy and the house "where the ceiling is air" is her noble parents' *palazzo*.

Andantino
pp dolce
Con-nais tu le pa-ys où fleu-rit l'o-ran-
Is that land known to you, where the or-ange trees
p
ger? Le pa-ys des fruits d'or et des ros-es ver-
grow, Where the o-live and pine grace the hill-side to-
meilles, Où la brise est plus douce et l'oi-seau plus lé-
geth-er, Where the quail swift-er fly through an air more a-
ger, Où dans tou-te sai-son bu-ti-nent les a-
glow, Where the bees hum all year in rose flow-er-ing

sempre dolce
beil-les, Où ra-yonne et sou-rit, comme un bien-fait de
weath-er, Where the boun-ties of God so lov-ing-ly re-
poco cresc.
dim.
Dieu, Un é-ter-nel prin-temps sous un ciel tou-jours bleu!
new: Mild ev-er-last-ing Spring un-der skies ev-er blue!
piu mosso
Hé-las! Que ne puis-je te sui-vre Vers ce ri-vage heu-
A-las! As I wan-der for-ev-er Far from that hap-py
pp
p
f
reux d'où le sort m'e-xi-la! C'est là, c'est là que je vou-drais
shore, Far-ther still wan-der I! O God! if ev-er I could go
mf

vi — vre, Ai - mer, ai - mer et mou - rir! — C'est là que je vou - drais
there once more To live, to love and to die — Ah! There to be and in
vi — vre, c'est là! oui, — c'est là!
bliss once more To live, love — and die!
Allegretto
Ped.
rit.
dim.

p Andantino
Con— nais-tu la mai-son où l'on m'at-tend là-
Is— that house known to you where the ceil—ing is
p
bas?— La sal-le aux lam-bris d'or,— où des hom-mes de
air?— And down through frames of gold— there are cher-ub-im
dim.
mar—bre m'ap-pel—lent dans la nuit—
glanc—ing, Where mar—ble men at night—
pp
pp
—en me ten-dant les bras?— Et la cour où l'on
—lead me down a great stair,— To a court-yard with

dan — se — à l'om — bre d'un grand ar — bre?
hun — dreds — be-neath one bay-tree danc-ing?
Et le lac trans-pa-rent où glis — sent sur les
On a sha — dow-less lake un — num — bered sails of
eaux mil — le ba-teaux lé-gers pa-reils à des oi-
white Gleam as they skim a-bout like swal — lows in their
dim.
p
seaux
flight
Hé-las!
A-las!
Que ne puis-je te
as I wan-der for-
pp

sui - vre Vers ce pa - ys loin-tain d'où le sort m'e-xi - la! C'est là c'est
ev - er Far from that hap-py shore, Far-ther still wan-der I! O God! if
là que je vou-drais vi - vre, Ai - mer, ai - mer et mou - rir! C'est
ev - er I could go there once more To live, to love and to die Ah!
là que je vou-drais vi - vre, c'est là! oui, c'est là!
There to be and in bliss once more To live, love and die!
p
f
mf
Ped.
*
dim.
pp

CELESTE AÏDA

FROM AÏDA

BY GIUSEPPE VERDI

LIBRETTO BY ANTONIO GHISLANZONI

First performance at Cairo Opera House, Cairo, Egypt, December 24, 1871

In the opening lines of the opera, Ramfis, the high priest of Egypt, tells a young officer named Radames that the Ethiopians are again on the warpath and that a brave and able young soldier is to be appointed general for the defense campaign. Left alone, Radames hopes that he may receive the appointment, and that after he has won the campaign he may marry his beloved Aïda, a daughter of the enemy, who is a slave to the Egyptian Princess Amneris. Should he succeed, he will return Aïda to her beautiful native land and a throne near the sun.

As suggested by the text, the quietly flowing line of the melody, and the accompaniment, the aria is the expression of a dream and should be sung in a dream-like style. It seldom is. For it is the tenor's only aria in the entire opera; it has to be sung a few moments after the rise of the curtain and before the singer has warmed into his work; and the temptation to be safe and sing loud is almost irresistible. One brave tenor (through a mediary, it is true) pointed out to Verdi the near impossibility of taking the last high note pianissimo as the score demands. Rather grudgingly, the composer gave his consent to sing it loud, provided the last four syllables were repeated softly and an octave lower at the end. One may hear it done this way by Richard Tucker in the recording of *Aïda* prepared by Arturo Toscanini.

Andantino
Radames: con espress.
Original in Bb
p
Ce - le - ste A - ï - da, for - ma di - vi - na,
A - ï - da be - lov - ed, vi - sion of beau - ty
ppp
p espr.
dolce
pp
mi - sti - co ser - to di lu - ce e fior.
Where earth and heav - en match - less - ly pair.
8va
Ped.
portando
del mio pen - sie - ro tu sei re - gi - na, tu di mia
No oth - er beau - ty makes me its cap - tive, No oth - er
vi - ta sei lo splen - dor.
love would I make my care!
espr.
p

244

sempre dolciss.
Il tuo bel cie - lo vor - rei ri -
O that I could to your coun - try re -
dar - ti, le dol - ci brez - ze del pa - trio
store you, There in its free - dom our love would be
animato un poco
suol: un re - gal ser - to sul crin po -
owned; Far from all splen - dor, splen - did I'd
con entusiasmo
f
sar - ti, er - ger - ti un tro — no vi - ci - no al
see you Un - der your sky — in my love en-
f
col canto

sol, ah! Ce le ste A-
throned! O! A ï - da be-
p leggeriss.
espr.
ï da, for ma di
lov ed, vis ion of
vi na, mi sti - co
beau ty, Where earth and
pp
rag gio di lu - ce e
heav en match less - ly

fior, del mio pen -
pair. No oth er
p
sie ro tu sei re -
beau ty makes me its
gi na, tu di mia vi - ta sei lo splen-
cap tive, No oth - er love would I make my
ppp quasi parlando
dor Il tuo bel cie - lo vor - rei ri
care! O to your coun - try could I re-
p

dar - ti, le dol - ci brez - ze del pa - trio suol; un re - gal
store you, In free-dom there would our love be owned; Far from all
sempre p
animando
f
ser - to sul crin po - sar - ti, er - ger - tiun
splen - dor, splen - did I'd see you Un - der your
cresc.
f
col canto
ppp
dim.
tro - no vi - ci - no al sol, un tro - no vi - ci - no al
sky in my love en - throned, By love you would be en-
ppp
leggermente
morendo
sol, un tro - no vi - ci - no al sol!
throned, By love you would be en - throned!
p
ppp
rit.
morendo

ERI TU

FROM UN BALLO IN MASCHERA

BY GIUSEPPE VERDI

LIBRETTO BY ANTONIO SOMMA

First performance at Teatro Apollo, Rome, February 17, 1859

Renato, secretary and privy councilor to Riccardo, has discovered his wife in a melodramatically embarrassing (though actually quite innocent) meeting with his patron. It happened at midnight underneath a gallows on a cold hillside, and it was witnessed by a pair of villainous and grinning courtiers. When Renato gets his wife home, he tells her that he is going to kill her, and she begs only to be allowed to go to their little son's room to bid him good-by.

Left alone, Renato relents somewhat and decides to take his vengeance instead on the party he regards as even more guilty than his wife—his friend and benefactor Riccardo. There is a portrait of this noble gentleman hanging on the wall, and it is to this picture that Renato addresses his strongly contrasted emotions of anger and sorrow.

The fact that the scene of this opera is sometimes laid in Stockholm, sometimes in colonial Boston, sometimes in Naples, while the names, ranks, and even the colors of some of the characters are altered along with the geography, bears some testimony to the power of music to make strong elementary emotions universally understood.

Andante sostenuto
mf
E - ri tu che mac-
It was you who cor-
mf
p
p
chia vi quel - l'a - ni - ma, la de-
rup - ted the soul I loved, Once the
p
dolce
li - zia dell' a - ni - ma mi - a che m'af-
star that my own soul took light from! In a
p
f
fi - di e d'un trat-to ese - cra - bi - le l'u - ni-
mo - ment you be-reft me of ev - 'ry-thing That has
f
f

ver - so av - ve - le - ni per me, av - ve - le - ni per
ev - er had mean - ing for me Or was sac - red to
me! Tra - di - tor! che com - pen - si in tal
me! You be - trayed both my faith and my
gui - sa dell' a - mi - co tuo pri - mo, del - l'a - mi - co tuo pri - mo la
friend - ship Though you knew that my life was ev - er yours And it ev - er would
fè!
be!
cantabile espressivo

espress.
O dol-cez — ze per-du — te! O me-
O the dear lost en-chant - ments, O
mo — rie d'un am-ples — so che l'es — se — re in
me — mo - ry Of the deep calm in love's ten - der
di — a! quan - do A-me — lia si bel — la, si
ec — sta - sy When A - me — lia, all can — dor, all

can di - da sul mio se no bril - la va d'a -
love li - ness With a soft glance would her love im -
mor! quan - d'A-me lia sul mio
part! When Am-e lia Came with
se-no bril - la - va d'a-more, bril - la - va d'a-mor! È fi -
love to my arms and with love Ev - er looked on me! It is
ni - ta: non sie-de che l'o dio, non sie-de che
ov - er! Now noth-ing but hat red, now noth-ing but
pp
p
f
ff

dim.
l'o-dio, che l'o-dio e la mor-te nel ve - do-vo cor!
hat-red And ran-cor have place an-y more in my heart!
ppp
p
O dol-cez ze per du
O the dear lost en chant
te! O sper-an - ze d'a-mor, d'a mor, d'a
ments Gone be-yond hope with love, with love, with
col canto
mor!
love!
pp
f
pp

QUESTA O QUELLA

FROM RIGOLETTO

BY GIUSEPPE VERDI

LIBRETTO BY FRANCESCO MARIA PIAVE

First performance at Teatro La Fenice, Venice, March 11, 1851

The opera opens with a ball that the Duke of Mantua is giving for his courtiers. He himself is enjoying it as thoroughly as any of his guests, joking with some of the courtiers, and delivering his dangerously irresponsible philosophy of love in this little aria. Its bouncy, almost offhand rhythm, even its momentary wandering from the simple, basic harmonies, suggest perfectly the lighthearted and unreliable character of this Don Juanesque duke. Immediately he is through with the song, he takes the Countess Ceprano—much to the Count's discomfort—as his partner in a minuet which Verdi modeled, consciously or not, on the more famous one from Mozart's *Don Giovanni.*

The libretto follows rather closely Victor Hugo's *Le roi s'amuse,* with King Francis I as its libertine villain. For political reasons the historical King had to be changed to a fictitious duke in the opera. Only one aspect of the many-faceted character of Francis is depicted in either play or opera—his delight in seduction as an indoor sport, as projected in *Questa o quella.*

Original in A♭
con eleganza
p
staccato
p
Ques - ta o quel — la — per me pa - ri so - no a quan - t'al — tre d'in tor - no — d'in - tor - no mi ve — do:
Ev' - ry beau — ty — is e - qual to a - ny That I see — And I hail them — as crowns of cre — a — tion.
del mio co — re — l'im - pe - ro non ce — do — me - glio ad u — na —
Yet no wo — man — pre - sents a temp - ta — tion — Quite so sing - u - lar, —

che ad al - tra bel - tà.
that she crowns the lot!
La co - sto - ro ad - ve -
If on one day my
nen - za è qual do - no
gra - cious ex - cite - ment
con brio
di che il fa - to ne in -
Be on some love in
fio - ra la vi - ta
all faith ex - ten - ded,
s'og - gi que - sta
By the next, or
mi tor - na gra - di - ta, for - se u - n'al - tra, for - se u - n'al - tra
be - fore day be end - ed, For an - oth - er, say More nov - el

57

do-man lo sa - rà u - n'al tra, for se u-
I lov - ing - ly plot, or I may love her
n'al tra do - man lo sa - rà.
two days, to va - ry the plot!
p
rinf.
p
La co -
All the
p
stan - za, ti - ran - na del co - re, ae - te - stia mo qual
faith - ful are slaves of a ty - rant Or mere dod - der - ing

mor - bo, qual mor - bo cru - de - le; Sol chi
Beg - gars un - ab - le to wan - der; Love has
vuo - le si ser - ba fe - de - le; non v'ha a -
lib - e - ral fa - vors to squan - der And is not
mor, se non v'è li - ber - tà. De' ma -
love where its free-dom is not. For the
ri - ti il ge - lo - so fu - ro - re, degli a -
poor jea-lous men wo - men mar - ry Or their

con brio
man — ti le sma — nie de - ri — do: — an - co
lov — ers, I save — my de - ri — sion: — Though they
d'Ar - go — i cen - t'oc-chi di - sfi - do se mi pun - ge, se mi
chain them, — if I make a de - cis - ion That I want them, say, to
pun - ge — u - na qual-che bel - tà — se —
love — me, — They will quick-ly be got! — Ah! —
mi — pun - ge — u - na qual-che bel - tà.
Those that move me yield — and are quick-ly for - got!
p
f

LA DONNA È MOBILE

FROM RIGOLETTO

BY GIUSEPPE VERDI

LIBRETTO BY FRANCESCO MARIA PIAVE

First performance at Teatro La Fenice, Venice, March 11, 1851

In the last act of the opera the Duke, disguised as a common soldier, is the overnight guest of Sparafucile, a sinister fellow who runs a disreputable inn with his sister as chief attraction and who doubles as a professional assassin whenever he can drum up business. As the Duke pours himself wine and shuffles a pack of cards, he gives his unflattering opinion of the opposite sex in *La donna è mobile,* the catchiest and best-known tune in the opera. Most tenors interpolate a little cadenza and a high note at the end in order to increase the applause. Some even throw the pack of cards into the air, just to make sure.

Later in the act Sparafucile murders the opera's heroine, Gilda, stuffs her body into a bag, and delivers it to the hunchback Rigoletto. Rigoletto thinks he is dragging out the body of the Duke, whom he has hired Sparafucile to murder. At that moment the Duke's voice is heard from inside the inn again singing *La donna è mobile.* Horrified, Rigoletto tears open the bag and finds, instead of the Duke, his own daughter.

So confident was Verdi that this tune would be a great hit that he kept it to himself till the last possible moment, letting the tenor see it only a few days before the opening night and enjoining complete secrecy on him and others around the opera house. His calculation turned out to be quite correct.

Allegretto
Original in B Major
p marcato
con brio
La don - na è mo - bi - le qual piu - ma al ven - to,
Wo - men are wea - ther vanes, Fick - le their choi - ces;
pp
mu - ta d'ac - cen - to e di pen - sie - ro. Sem - pre un a - ma - bi - le,
Light - ly their voi - ces E - cho light na - tures. Fa - ces a - men - a - ble
pp
leg - gia - dro vi - so, in pian - to o in ri - so è men - zo - gne - ro.
Laugh - ing or cry - ing, Ev - er are ly - ing Lures of the crea - tures.

Second Verse:

Hearts that are given them,
Trusting them tender,
Find in surrender,
Cruelty wielded!

Yet he must equally
Find his life wasted,
Who has not tasted
Love they have yielded!

Women are nowhere
Happy to settle,
But in fine fettle
Float on the air!

È sempre misero chi a lei s'affida
Chi le confida, mal-cauto il cor!
Pur mai non sentesi, felice appieno
Chi su quel seno non liba amore!
La donna è mobil qual piuma al vento,
Muta d'accento e di pensier,
e di pensier,
e di pensier!

IL LACERATO SPIRITO

FROM SIMON BOCCANEGRA

BY GIUSEPPE VERDI

LIBRETTO BY FRANCESCO MARIA PIAVE AND ARRIGO BOÏTO

First performance at Teatro La Fenice, Venice, March 12, 1857

Of all the Verdi operas, not excluding *Il Trovatore, Simon Boccanegra* is the most obscure and complex in its plot. Fortunately for the present purposes, its best-known aria, *Il lacerato spirito,* occurs in the Prologue, the action of which precedes the complexities of Act I by twenty-four years. All that is necessary to know, then, for the dramatic background of this aria, is that the man who sings it is one Jacopo Fiesco, a Genoese nobleman of the fourteenth century, who has just lost his beloved daughter, Maria. He wanders disconsolately from the door of his palatial home and, after a recitative, sings this noble aria for basso while, indoors, the chorus intones a *Miserere* for the just-departed woman.

Fiesco is technically the villain of the play, for he is bitterly opposed to its hero, Boccanegra, for both political and personal reasons. Boccanegra is leader of the plebeian faction, Fiesco of the patrician; and Maria has borne an illegitimate daughter to Boccanegra. Nevertheless, Fiesco is a nobleman in nature as well as in rank, and his strength of character is well reflected in the music Verdi composed for him, especially in this aria.

Original in F# minor
Andante sostenuto
p
Fiesco
Il la — ce — ra — to spi — ri — to
Sharp is pa — ter — nal suf — fer — ing,
pp
del me — sto ge — ni — to — re
Deep as the soul's dam — na — tion,
e — ra ser - ba — to stra — zio d'in -
When once the name of fa — ther Is
65

fa - miae di do — lo — re.
lost in de — pri — va — tion.
Chorus:
È
De-
mor — ta!
par — ed!
è
De —
mor — ta!
par — ted!
Mi - se - re - re!
Mi - se-
re - re!
cantabile
Il ses — to a lei de'
May she who suf - fered
espr.
pp
mar — ti - ri pie — to — so il cie — lo
mar — tyr - dom, In hea — ven ra — diant
È mor — ta!
De - par — ted!

die Re sa al ful - gor de-
be: There ev er in be-
è mor - ta!
De - par - ted!
gli an ge - li, pre ga, Ma - ria, per
a ti - tude, Pray, O Ma - ria, for
mi se re re!
Mi se re re!
è mor ta!
De - par ted!
me,
me!
a lei s'a - pron le sfe re!
The gates of bliss have op ened!
Mi - se - re re!
re sa al ful - gor degli an ge - li
There ev er in be a ti - tude,
Mi se -

pre — ga, Ma - ria, per me
Pray, O Ma - ria, for me!
L.H.
R.H.
re - re!
Mai più mon la ve-
The bright an - gel - ic
pre - ga per me,
O pray for me!
drem in ter — ra!
host re - ceives her!
Mi - se - re - re
pre - ga per me, pre - ga, Ma - ria, per
O pray for me, O pray, Ma - ria, for
Mi - se - re - re
me.
me.
non la ve - drem mai più!
pp No more on earth is she!

BRINDISI

FROM LA TRAVIATA

BY GIUSEPPE VERDI

LIBRETTO BY FRANCESCO MARIA PIAVE

First performance at Teatro La Fenice, Venice, March 6, 1853

Violetta, one of the prettiest and most successful demimondaines of Paris in the 1830s, is having a party. A generous hostess, she permits her friends to bring other friends. One of the latter is Alfredo, a country-bred youth who has admired Violetta at a distance. She takes to him at once, seats him beside her at table, flirts with him, and seconds a request that he sing a drinking song. He sings, then, the first stanza of the *Brindisi,* holding his glass up toward Violetta, in compliment, on the words *poichè quello occhio al core onnipotente va.* Then, after the chorus repeats the tune, Violetta rises and sings the second stanza.

Allegretto
Alfredo:
p con grazio
pp leggero
Li - bia mo, li - bia - mo ne'
To plea sure, the god-dess, the
lie ti ca li - ci che la bel - lez - za in - fio
bright in con stan - cy, Plea - sure in whose de vo
ra, e la fug - ge - vol, fug - ge vol o
tion With fond in - ces - sant, in - ces sant mo
ra s'in - ne brii - a vo - lut tà.
tion We fol - low and for get.
Li -
To
pp

biam ne' dol - ci fre - mi - ti che su - sci - ta l'a
con - stant love who pa - tient - ly A - waits till we who
mo - re, poi - chè quell' oc - chio al co - re on -
doubt him Re - mem - ber that with - out him We
ni - po - ten - te va. Li - bia - mo a -
but pur - sue re - gret! Let wine though like
mo - re, a - mor fra i ca - li - ci più cal - di
plea - sure, a flee - ting re - vel - ry, Warm us in
p
pp

Chorus:
ba - ci a vrà. Ah! li - biam a mor fra'
love's name yet. Ah! May wine a flee - ting
ca - li ci più cal - di ba - ci a vrà.
re - vel ry Warm us in love's name yet!
8va
Violetta:
Tra vo i, tra vo - i sa - prò di - vi
What fol ly, what fol - ly to ask of an
- de - re il tem - po mio gio con do; tut
- y - thing More than its gift for giv ing; Ask

— to è fol - li - a, fol - li — a nel mon — do
— for no pur - pose, no pur - pose in liv — ing,
con grazia
ciò che non è pia — cer. La vi — ta è
Plea - sure can - not con — vey. True liv — ing
Alfredo:
nel tri — pu — dio, Quan - do non s'a - mi — an —
is a — ban — don, Which dies be - lied by —
Violetta:
co — ra Nol di — te a chi l'i —
true love, Which falls in turn to —

Alfredo:
gno ra. È il mio des - tin co sì
new love, The sad un - lov - ing say!
Violetta and
Alfredo: (with chorus)
Ah! Go - dia mo, la taz - za, la taz - za e il
Ah! In care less for - get - ful, for - get ful
pp
can ti - co la not - te ab - bel - la e il ri
pro di - gies Mo - ments take in - fin ite mea
so; in que sto, in que sto pa ra
sure, En chan ted, en chan ted on by
cresc.

di — so ne sco - pra il nuo - vo dì, ah!
plea — sure, The mo - ments can - not stay! No!
8va
sempre cresc.
ah! ne sco - pra il dì, ah! ah!
no! No mo - ment can stay, no! No!
8va
ne sco - pra il dì, ah!
No mo - ment can stay! Ah!
8va
f
sì.
no!
ff
8va
ff
Ped.

DI PROVENZA IL MAR

FROM LA TRAVIATA

BY GIUSEPPE VERDI

LIBRETTO BY FRANCESCO MARIA PIAVE

First performance at Teatro La Fenice, Venice, March 6, 1853

In Act II Violetta and Alfredo have been living happily together in a villa on the outskirts of Paris for some three months when the young man's father, Germont, pays Violetta a visit while his son is in town. The highly respectable old gentleman persuades the demimondaine that, for family reasons, she should give up his son, which she does promptly but with great anguish. When Alfredo comes home and finds her farewell note, his father tries to comfort him by urging him to return to their fair home in Provence.

The son listens with far less attention than the audience before the footlights usually does; for whatever music critics have to say against this aria (and they have said a great deal, even to pointing out uncharitably that it is like a travesty of a once-popular spurious work known as *Weber's Last Waltz*), *Di Provenza* is a fine showpiece for a baritone with a sympathetic ring to his voice.

Andante piùtosto mosso
Germont:
p
dolce
Di Pro - ven-za il mar, il suol chi dal
Can your heart be tru - ly won from Pro -
espr.
p
marc.
pp
cor ti can - cel - lò? Chi dal cor ti can - cel - lò? di Pro -
vence en - ti - re - ly, from Pro - vence your home and me, can your
dolce
ven-za il mar il suol? al na - tio ful - gen - te sol qual des -
heart be tru - ly won? From the com - fort of the sun and the
marc.
pp
ti - no ti fu - rò? qual des - ti - no ti fu - rò? al na -
blue re - viv - ing sea, from the blue re - viv - ing sea and the

277

tio ful - gen - te sol? Oh ram - men-ta pur nel duol ch'i - vi
com-fort of the sun? There your life was well be - gun, There you
pp
pp
dolce
gio - jaa te bril - lò, e che pa - ce co - là sol su te
grew a - las to flee all a well-born lov-ing son wants by
con express.
f
splen-de - re an-cor può, e che pa - ce co - là sol su te
na - ture or de - gree, all a well-born lov-ing son wants by
p
splen-de - re an-cor può. Dio mi gui - dò,
na - ture or de - gree. It waits at home!
8va

con forza
rall.
ppp
Dio mi gui - dò, Dio mi gui - dò!
It waits at home! It still can be!
8va
pp
p
espr.
allarg.
morendo
Ah il tuo
Could you
dolciss.
marc.
vec-chio ge - ni - tor, tu non sai quan-to sof - frì, tu non
feel and yet ig - nore what be - grieved a fa - ther so? What be -
pp
sai quan-to sof - frì, il tuo vec-chio ge - ni - tor! Te lon -
grieved a fa - ther so, could you feel and yet ig - nore? How I

dolce
marc.
ta - no, di squal-lor il suo tet - to si co - prì, il suo
suf-fered all the more in the grief you'd un - der - go, in the
pp
tet - to si co - prì, di squal - lo - re, di squal-lor ma seal -
grief that you would know How I suf - fered all the more! Still at
pp
pp
dolce
fin ti trovo an - cor, se in me spe me non fal - lì, se la
home an o - pen door waits and So - lace for all woe, love and
pp
con espress.
f
vo - ce dell' o - nor in te ap - pien non am - mu - tì, me seal -
ho - nor will re - store what was yours not long a - go. Love and

fin ti tro-voan-cor, se in me spe me non fal-lì,
hon-or will re-store what was yours not long a-go.
Dio m'e-sau-dì,
A peace-ful heart
8va
con forza
e rall.
ppp
Dio m'e-sau-dì, Dio m'e-sau-dì,
They will be-stow, they will be-stow
Dio m'e-sau-dì!
a peace-ful heart!
Ma,
O
8va
pp
p
f
dim. ed allarg.
ma se al fin ti tro-vo an cor, ti tro-vo an cor, Dio m'e-sau-dì, Dio m'e-sau-
we shall live as once be-fore, as once be-fore, A peace-ful heart love will be-
dì!
stow!
pp
Ped.
*

IL BALEN

FROM IL TROVATORE

BY GIUSEPPE VERDI

LIBRETTO BY SALVATORE CAMMARANO

First performance at Teatro Apollo, Rome, January 19, 1853

The Count di Luna, the villain of this opera, is madly in love with the heroine, Leonora, and is ready to go to any lengths to have her for his own. By the time we reach the second scene of Act II of the rather murky libretto, Leonora is about to take her vows as a nun because she believes her lover, the unknown troubadour, has been slain. Di Luna, hearing of her intention, invades the garden of the convent at the head of a band of ruffians, vowing to abduct her. After discussing the matter with his followers, he is left alone long enough to sing this warm and sympathetic melody, which was known to every parlor musicale in our fathers' days as *The Tempest of the Heart.* For the few minutes it takes to sing the aria, Di Luna sheds the anger, born of frustration, that seems to be his sole characteristic throughout the rest of the opera, and one almost likes him. Not for long, however. Just as he is about to seize the girl, the hero appears with *his* gang of followers and snatches the prize away.

Largo
cantabile
p
Il ba-len del suo sor-
In her eyes a smile has
p
cantabile
ri-so d'u-na stel-la vin-ce il rag-gio! Il ful-
pow-ers Van-quished star-light can-not ri-val; In their
gor del suo bel vi-so no-vo in fon-de no-vo in fon-de a me co-
gent-le im-age on-ly will my cour-age, Will my cour-age know re-
rag-gio. Ah! l'a-mor, l'a-mo-re on-d'ar-do le fa-
vi-val. Yet to love when love is but hope-less, Fires the
pp

dolce
vel- li in mi- o fa- vor! Sper-da il so- le d'un suo
hat- red deep in my will; O would she but smile con
dolce
squar- do la tem pe- sta del mio
sent- ing, that this rage might then be
con espansione
cor. Ah! l'a- mor l'a- mor on- d'ar- do, le fa- vel- li in mio fa-
still! For to love when love is hope-less, Fires the hat- red in my
f
dim
dolce
vo- re, Sper- da il so- le d'un suo sguar- do la tem- pes- ta del mio
will; Would she on- ly smile con- sent- ing That this rag- ing might be
pp

cor. Ah! l'a- mor l'a- mor on- d'ar- do le fa- vel- li in mio fa-
still! Ah! to love when love is hope-less, Fires the hat- red in my
vo- re, Sper- da il so— le d'un suo sguar- do la— tem- pes— ta,
will;— Would she on— ly smile con— sent— ing, That this rag- ing,
f
ah! la tem- pes- ta del mio
Ah! That this rag- ing might be
cor!
still!
p
pp
85

SIEGMUND'S LOVE SONG

FROM DIE WALKÜRE

BY RICHARD WAGNER

LIBRETTO BY THE COMPOSER

First performance at Hof-und-National Theater, Munich, January 26, 1870

Into the rude hut of a fierce warrior named Hunding staggers a weary, sorely pressed, and weaponless young man. Hunding's wife, Sieglinde, finds him on the hearth and is strangely attracted to him. When Hunding returns, he discovers that the young man is an enemy; but the laws of hospitality require that Siegmund be given refreshment and permitted to rest overnight. Hunding promises, however, that he will kill him the next day.

Sieglinde, however, gives her husband a sleeping potion and then returns to find out more about the mysterious guest. Not only does she find out that they are mutually attracted, but she also discovers that they are brother and sister. Various signs, natural and supernatural, including a sword embedded in a tree and a dramatic change in the weather from storm to bright moonlight, play on the emotions of the young couple. He sings her this passionate love song; she replies in accents no less ardent; and together they flee into the night.

Moderato
Original in Bb Major
pp dolce
p dolce ed espress.
Win — ter - stür - me wi - chen dem Won — ne — mond: — in
Win — ter storms o - bey The be — witch — ing god; — With
mil-dem Lich-te leuch-tet der Lenz; — auf lin-den Lüf — ten,
spells to still them, Spring is a - broad. — In light more gen — tle,
leicht und lieb — lich Wun-der we - bend er sich wiegt: durch
Jo - cund bree — zes, Ev'-ry-where his Won-ders glow; Through

cresc.
Wald und Au — en weht sein A — them, weit ge-öff-net lacht sein
field and fo — rest Fon-dly brea — thing, He in-spi-rits All to
Aug: — aus sel'-ger Vög-lein San-ge süss er tönt, —
life. — while hap-py bird-song hails His hoped ap-proach, —
hol-de Düf-te haucht er aus; Sei-nem war-men Blut ent-blü-hen
At his pas-sage Per-fumes rise.. By his warmth in-voked, the wood-land
won-ni-ge Blu-men Keim und Spross entspringt sein-er Kraft Mit
Wak-ens in flo — wer; No-thing may De-ny him his will. His

poco energico
zar — ter Waf — fen Zier be - zwingt er die Welt; —
ten — der call en - treat — ing Tri - umphs at once; —
p
mf
Win - ter und Sturm wi - chen der star - ken Wehr: — Wohl
Win - ter and storm wane At the won - d'rous runes; — And
p
piu cresc.
muss - te den tap - fern Streich - en die stren - ge Thü - re auch weich - en, die
ob - stin - ate doors that barred All his blest en - dear - ments from reach - ing our
p
cresc.
f
trot - zig und starr uns trenn - te von ihm!
hearts in their sleep, Must o — pen to him!
f
p espr.
Ped.
6
6
6
*

molto cresc.
mf
f
Zu sei ner Schwe ster schwang
His dream ing sis ter Drew
più f
ff
dim.
p
er Sich her; die Lie
him to her; Here love
p
f
dolce
p
be lock te den Lenz: In
had wan ted to wake, The
f
dim.
p

tranquillo
uns' rem Bu sen barg sie sich
love we both Had bu ried with-
pp
con anima
f
tief; nun lacht sie se lig dem
in, And now in light can be
cresc.
Licht
known!
p
Die
Her
f
ff
dim.
bräut - li - che Schwe - ster be - frei - te der Bru der; zer -
bro - ther has come for The bride to re - lease her, Her

cresc.
trüm — mert liegt, was je sie ge - trennt;
win — t'ry shack — les Shat - ter and fall;
p
f
f
jauch - zend grüsst sich das jun — ge Paar: ver -
Free — ly joy — ous They join in praise: U -
p dolce
f
f
eint — sind
ni — ted are
p
cresc.
f
Lie — be und Lenz!
Love — now and Spring!
mf
f

THE PRIZE SONG

FROM DIE MEISTERSINGER VON NÜRNBERG

BY RICHARD WAGNER

LIBRETTO BY THE COMPOSER

First performance at Hof-und-National Theater, Munich, June 21, 1868

In the first act of *Die Meistersinger,* a young Franconian knight passing through the medieval town of Nuremburg, falls in love at first sight with the fair Eva, daughter of the goldsmith Pogner. As Eva is to be the prize for the winner of a song contest to take place the next day, Walter at once takes the test of admission to the mastersingers' guild and is ignominiously rejected. He stays the night at the home of Hans Sachs, shoemaker and the most respected of the mastersingers, and the next morning relates to his host a glorious dream he has had. So wonderful are both the words of this recital and the melody Walter sings, that Sachs jots down the verses and encourages the young man to try for the prize. Needless to say, as *Die Meistersinger* is a comedy and Walter its juvenile lead, he wins the girl.

Snatches of this melody, in the shape of leitmotifs, are used throughout the opera, beginning with the Prelude. It is only in the last act, when Walter offers the song in competition, that it is heard in its entirety and uninterruptedly.

Moderato molto
dolce
Original in C
Mor - gen - licht leuch-tend im ro — si - gen Schein, von Blüth und
Morn - ing had new - ly in ra — di - ance clad The air that
cresc.
Duft ge-schwellt die Luft, voll al - ler Won — nen, nie er - son-nen, ein
knows The wak-ened rose; The danc-ing light — re - vealed a gar - den Where
dim.
dim.
poco pui lento
dolciss.
Gar - ten lud mich — ein, dort un - ter ei - nem Wun - der - baum, von
I a vi — sion — had! For there be-neath a glow-ing tree, The
dolciss.
poco pui lento
Früchten reich be — han-gen, zu schau'n im sel'- gen Lie - bes traum, was
quest - ed tree of Hea-ven, All love could ask a — wait — ed me, All
cresc.

poco a poco pi u mosso
höch-stem Lust-ver-lan-gen Er-fül-lung kühn ver-hiess, das schön-ste
love dare dream was gi-ven! It would a dream suf-fice: In truth I
p
poco a poco pi u mosso
f
Weib
woke!
dolce
E — va im Pa-ra-dies!
Eve stood in Pa-ra-dise!
f
6
6
6
dim.
p
p
dolciss.
pp
A — bend — lich
Ev' — ning drew
p
3
däm-mernd — um-schloss mich die Nacht; auf stei-lem Pfad war ich ge-
on in — to deep-en — ing shade: As tho' at will I climbed a
3

naht zu ei-ner Quel — le rei-ner Wel — le, die
hill To where a nev — er ceas-ing foun — tain In
dim.
3
p rit.
lock-end mir — ge-lacht: dort un-ter ei-nem Lor-beer-baum von
cry-stal mu — sic played be-neath an an-cient lau-rel tree By
3
pp
Ster-nen hell durch — schie — nen, ich schaut' im wa-chen
star-ry light dis — cov — ered, All that the po — et
cresc.
Dich-ter-traum, von hei-lig hol — den Mie — nen, mich
dreams to see Was to my wak — ing — of — fered: To
dim.
p

f
net-zend mit dem ed-len Nass das hehr-ste Weib:
drink the foun-tain which im-bues In-spir-ed song,
cresc.
f
6
6
p
die Mu — se des Par nass!
Par-nas — sus, Eve my Muse!
pp
f
p dolce
con fuoco
Huld — reich — ster Tag dem ich aus Dich-ter's Traum er-
Why did I wake? Were not my vi-sions true e-
p
cresc.
f
wacht! Dass ich er-traümt, das Pa-ra-dies, in himmlisch
nough? O day in — spired, I woke to see The ho-ly

neu — ver-klärter Pracht — hell vor mir lag, da-
realms — of art and love — still mine to take! The
f
hin lach-end nun die Quell den Pfad mir wies; — die
rose gar - den of the morn, the an — cient tree, — The
espr.
cresc.
dort ge — bo — ren, mein Herz er -
liv — ing foun — tain where song is
p dolce
p
ko — ren der Er - de lieb - lich - stes Bild, als Mu - se mir ge-
born, — And still the Muse wel-comed me To grace what shall be
p dolce
cresc.

weiht so hei — lig ernst als mild ward
done, To smile — on what must be So
cresc.
p
cresc.
kühn von mir ge-freit am lich — ten Tag der
dream and truth be one And I in song for-
f
p dolce
Son-nen, durch San — ges Sieg ge won — nen Par — nass
ev-er twice Par-nas — sus gain and Pa-ra-dise The prize
p
cresc. molto
poco rit. a tempo
und Pa-ra-dies.
in Eve is won!
poco rit.
f
a tempo

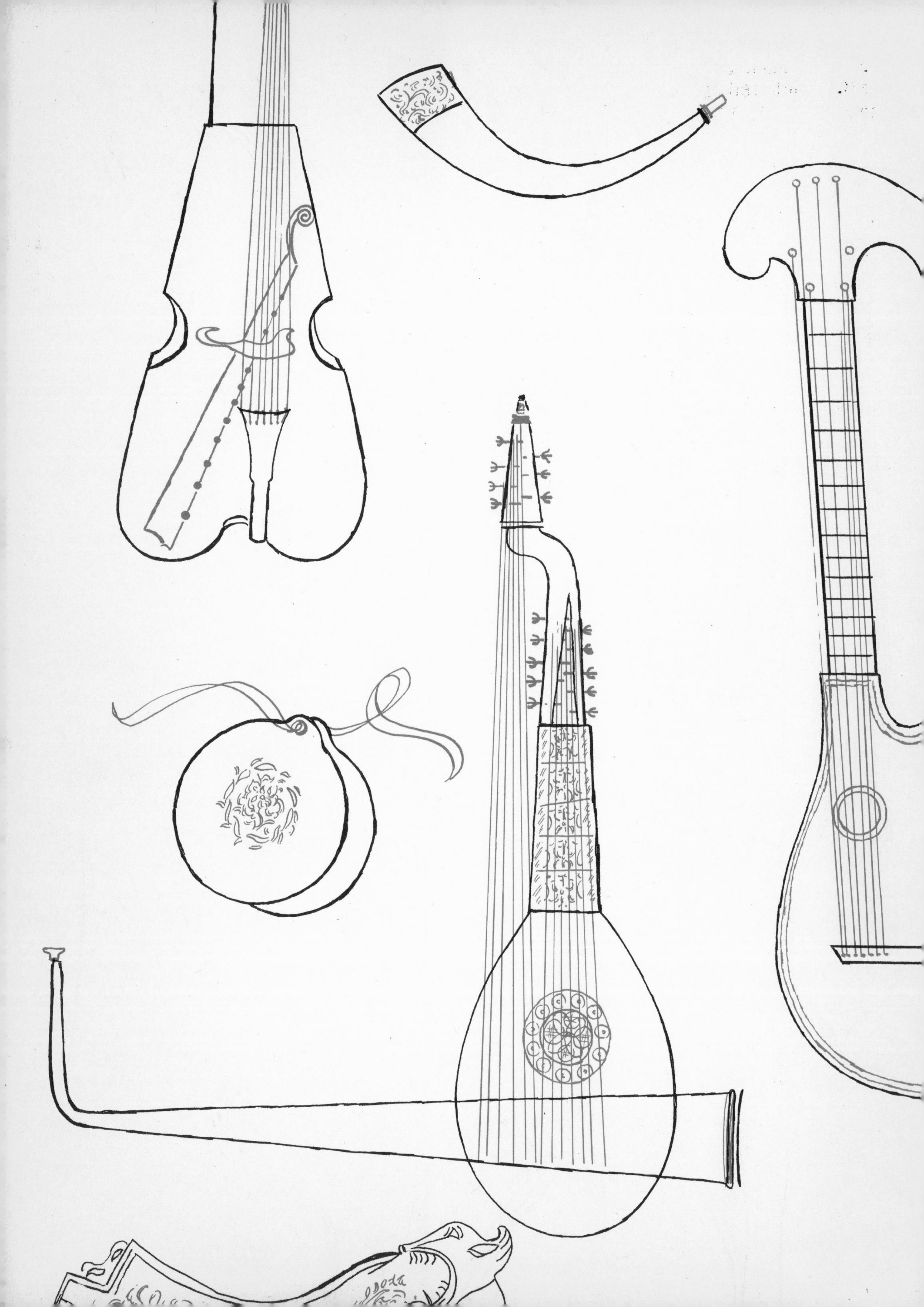